Music and Musi
Instruments in t..
World of Islam

Jean Jenkins
and
Poul Rovsing Olsen

Line drawings by John Pringle

World of Islam Festival Publishing Company Ltd

World of Islam Festival Publishing Company Ltd., London
© Jean Jenkins and Poul Rovsing Olsen

First published 1976
ISBN 0 905035 11 9 cased
ISBN 0 905035 12 7 paper

Published and produced by the World of Islam Festival Publishing Company Ltd.

Designed by Colin Larkin
Edited by Liz Évora
Set in 12/14pt Monophoto Plantin 110
Printed on 115 gsm Blade coated cartridge

Colour origination: Westerham Press
Filmset by Westerham Press and printed in England by Westerham Press Ltd., Westerham, Kent.

Front cover: detail from the *Khamsah Niẓāmī*, Persia 1539–43, showing lute (*'ud*) player accompanied by a frame drum (*daira*).
Backcover: detail of the ornamentation of the Afghan *rubab* (**G4**).

Contents

Acknowledgments

Work on the exhibition 'Music and Musical Instruments in the World of Islam' has included collecting the instruments and information, recording musicians, and photographing both makers and players in more than twenty countries, as well as writing the catalogue and preparing the gramophone records and sound tracks. Such a task, however inadequately performed, has depended on the help of more people than can be mentioned in this brief space.

Most grateful thanks go to our colleagues and friends in museums, universities, broadcasting and the teaching professions in the following countries: Afghanistan, Algeria, Egypt, India, Indonesia, Iran, Iraq, Jordan, Malaysia, Morocco, Niger, Nigeria, Pakistan, Syria, Tunisia, Turkey, Uganda, and Yemen. We are also extremely grateful to those who, over the years, have contributed to our work towards this exhibition: in Bulgaria, China, Ethiopia, France, Spain, Tanzania and Thailand. To certain of them our debt is especially profound, for their time and efforts to make this work productive: in Afghanistan, Diana Colvin of the British Institute in Afghanistan; in Algeria, Pierre Augier of the Centre for Anthropological, Ethnological and Prehistoric Research; in India, Dr Sachin Roy of the National Museum in Delhi, Narpath Singh of the Jodhpur Academy of Folk Music and Kamal Kothari of the Borunda section of that Academy; in Iran, Audrey Lambert of the British Council, Fozieh Madj of Iran Television, and David Stronach and Alexander Morton of the British Institute of Persian Studies; in Morocco, Marc Loopuyt in Fez and Louis Soret in Marrakesh; in Niger, Albert Ferral of the National Museum of Niger; in Syria, Dr Bachir Zoudi of the National Museum and John and Pamela Bunney of the British Embassy; in Turkey, Dr Gültukin Oransay of the University of Ankara and Etem Üngör in Istanbul; as well as to colleagues and friends in Britain, Denmark and France who gave information, time and introductions which produced many successful results. Professor Laurence Picken of Cambridge University was especially helpful in this respect.

In addition, we extend our thanks to those who have loaned instruments: Lisette Davies, Dr Mark Littlewood, Emma Parsons and John Pringle.

For work on the exhibition, Milfie Howell and Carl Patterson have done the conservation and the former has also accessioned all the shipment of instruments. Hero Granger-Taylor has done the iconography. Insofar as the catalogue is concerned, John Pringle has made the line drawings, William Conner worked on the bibliography, and Kate Harney has typed the manuscript. The Horniman Museum has allowed its musicologist time to collect the instruments. The funds for field research, collecting the instruments and mounting the exhibition have been generously provided by the World of Islam Festival Trust. To all these we extend our heartfelt thanks.

Jean Jenkins
London 1976

General Introduction

Music and Musical Instruments

'Music and Musical Instruments in the World of Islam' is an attempt to present the major aspects of the subject in one exhibition. The instruments and their makers, the music and the musicians can be both seen and heard. The instruments, it is true, are displayed for safety's sake in glass cases, but the screens show hundreds of pictures of those instruments being made and played, and music recorded on them can be heard at the same time. Concerts in the exhibition hall itself will give London music-lovers a chance to hear some of the outstanding musicians in the Islamic world, and lecture demonstrations on their instruments will help people to understand the music and how it is produced. The series of gramophone records and cassettes, following the lines of this exhibition and its catalogue, will enable people to familiarize themselves in their own homes with a vast selection of music from the Islamic world.

In defining the scope of the world of Islam, we have included not only the Middle East, but all of Islamic Africa and South-east Asia. In addition, the influences of Islamic music and musical instruments on such far-flung areas as China (and through China on the whole of the Far East) and upon Europe have been included, as well as the return influences of western music upon the Islamic world.

As vast a field as this demands a series of detailed studies. This is impossible for a museum exhibition, so we have compromised in the following fashion: for the general public, who may be unfamiliar with music from the Islamic world, we have arranged both the exhibition and the catalogue so that the four main types of classical music practised in Islamic countries are displayed and discussed as entities, and the remaining instruments are presented typologically rather than geographically. The records have also followed these main groupings: the human voice, lutes, fiddles and strings, flutes and trumpets, reeds and bagpipes, and drums and rhythms. For the specialist, or those who want to continue the study of Islamic music, we have attempted to give a fairly comprehensive bibliography.

The Human Voice

The human voice is as important—if not more so—as the instruments in music in Islamic areas. Before the year 622 the practice of music in South-west Asia included a great number of different instruments and styles of singing from the various regions. *The Arabian Nights*, for example, tells of the princess whose slave brought, in the twinkling of an eye, a Damascus lute, a Persian harp, a Tartar pipe and an Egyptian dulcimer, showing that the musical life was as varied as that of London today. Although there is no prohibition against music in the Qu'ran itself, and it is known that music was played both at the wedding of the Prophet and, later, of his daughter, the austerity of the legalists who followed outlawed music. Even the cantilation of the Qu'ran was called 'reading' rather than singing although both melody and vocal ornamentation are beautifully presented there, and, to a lesser extent, in the *adhan* or call to Prayer. The condemnation of music was largely unsuccessful. Indeed, within Islam itself the mystic Sufi sects gave music a privileged place at their ceremonies. The religious leaders, the *khalifs*, entertained the noted musicians of their reigns at court. The great philosophers, like Al-Kīndī, Al-Farābi, Avicenna and Safi al-Din wrote profusely on musical theory and through the study of music they inevitably encouraged the making of it.

Even in later years music has been considered undesirable in some countries. But if classical music in many regions has admittedly lost some of its former strength, folk music continues to show extraordinary vitality. It is a necessity in the life of the peasants and villagers, blossoming in a wealth of forms, leaving us with the impression that the Islamic peoples, faithful to their musical traditions, have kept a deep faith in their own identity.

Melody

Music can exist without melody, but this is very rare. Melody is normally an important part of most kinds of music. In most parts of the world, melody is considered a basic musical element and this is the case in the Islamic world. Islamic music develops with the human voice as its starting point and to quite a high degree Islamic music consists of singing, so that the primary object of most instruments is to deliver an accompaniment to songs or to render special versions of songs. Ornamentation plays a role in many kinds of songs in the Middle East, but certainly not in all of them (songs of bedouins may thus often be entirely without ornaments). Ornaments may be found in abundance in religious chanting as for instance in the most common styles of Qu'ran reading (no Muslim would call this 'singing'; he would stress the term 'reading' although melodies are developed) and in the classical music such as in the virtuoso singing of the great Persian singers of *dastgah*, the Iraqian *maqām* singing and the *Layāli* singing in Egypt and other Mediterranean countries.

But what is the basic material of an Islamic melody? The Berbers (Kabyles, Tuaregs) of Maghreb and the western part of the Sahara more often than not confine their music to pentatonic scales (i.e. scales using five different pitches within an octave). The same is true of many East African peoples, and in Indonesia there are pentatonic scales of a quite original kind, since the five intervals may be of almost the same size: the so-called *Slendro*-scale.

In the greater part of the Middle East the melodic basis is an entirely different one. An amazing number of the tunes (and especially the tunes of the nomadic peoples) develop within a fourth or a fifth and are consequently labelled by many scholars with the Greek words: tetracordal and pentacordal. Sometimes the range may be even more restricted than that, being a kind of third or second, or may even be non-existent, as in some work songs which are confined to one single tone. But the fourth has proved to be of exceptional importance, as it is a basic interval in all Middle Eastern kinds of classical music. A fourth can be filled out in a number of ways and each tetracord has its specific name and thus represents what is generally called the bulk of *jins* in Middle Eastern music. The refined music of the courts naturally needed a greater range than a fourth can offer. The general name for a mode may be *maqām*, as is often the case in the Arab world, *makam*, which is the Turkish term, or *dastgah* and *avaz*, to use the Persian words. In any case we are confronted with combinations of *jins* which together cover up to two octaves and have a different aspect in the descending and ascending lines. In such a mode some of the tones may have a special importance, some being prominent and others insecure, being ordinary starting points or final points in a phrase. And each mode may be referred to a certain mood and to a particular season or part of the day. Even if these last-named characteristics have had their day in the Middle East and are only vaguely felt nowadays, they are surely inherent in the modal system of Pakistan and North India, a system of *ragas* which is otherwise quite similar to the systems of the Persians, Turks and Arabs.

When you have chosen your mode, you will normally remain in it, as long as the piece lasts, if you are a Pakistani or a North Indian. Many Turkish or Arab musicians would think it desirable to modulate to one or two other modes once the initial one is well established, but they would unerringly go back to the main mode before finishing. A Persian and even an Iraqi might very well present a whole spectrum of different modes, *jins*, leaving the initial *dastgah* or *maqām* almost at once and not necessarily returning to it before the end of the performance.

Melody is everywhere in the world of Islam. It accompanies its peoples from birth to death, inspires their work, fills their feasts with joy and may deepen their religious feelings. But if melody in these countries has a remarkable force, so has rhythm. We will discuss Islamic rhythms in some detail in the section devoted to drums and rhythm.

Names of Instruments

If you look at the photographs in this catalogue, you may be surprised to see that some form of the word *rabāb* (*rubāb, rebāb, rebaba* etc.) is used for the one-stringed bedouin spike fiddle as well as for the elaborate Malaysian one, but clearly those two instruments belong to the same group however geographically separated and differing in decoration. It becomes more difficult to see why the name is also applied to the classical fiddle of North Africa, or to the short plucked lute with a deep and waisted body called the Afghan *rubab*, and to the barbed lute with a very long neck from Chinese Turkestan called the Kashgar *rubab*, or, even more strangely, to the Sudanese lyre called in Ethiopia, and as far as Hyderabad in the Deccan, *rebaba*. But when that same lyre is known as a *tambura* in Bahrain, the confusion is compounded, for *tambura* (*tambor, tanbur, tampura*, etc.) is another wide-spread name referring to very different instruments: the Turkish classical lute with an extremely long neck, the Indian string drone with open strings, and the small Kurdish fretted lute used by some dervishes to put themselves into a trance. More strangely still, we ourselves apply it to a small frame drum with jingles: the tambourine.

The Turkish word *saz* is merely a generic word meaning musical instrument, but it is generally used for a type of long necked lute. Nevertheless, you will find an oboe of the Qashqai nomads of southern Persia also called *saz*. *Chang* is even odder: the harp shown in so many Persian miniatures was known as *chang*, but that name is applied to the Persian *santur* when it is played by the Turkic-speaking Uzbeks of Soviet Central Asia, and, curiously enough, to the small jew's harp of Afghanistan. The *kemençe* of classical Turkish music is a tiny, beautifully made instrument hollowed out of a single block of wood, but the same word refers to the spike fiddle of classical Persian music, with very different origins and appearance.

Instruments using the word *ṭar* are even more varied. The word itself means 'string', and it is true that the Indian *ektar* does have one string, and we usually find that *dutars* have two strings. But the Persian *sehtar* of today has four, rather than three, and the Indian *sitar* has a variable number (even if we discount entirely the sympathetic strings). Our guitar and the ancient Greek *kithara* (a square-bodied lyre) are completely different instruments; indeed, one could continue almost ad infinitum citing instances of the same word applying to instruments which look and sound very unlike each other and which are, moreover, used for widely disparate types of music.

The reverse of this process is perhaps more easily understood. It would seem logical that people who speak different languages should apply their own names to an instrument used in their own areas. Thus we find that the simple spike fiddle called *rebāb* or *rabāb* or *rebaba* by the nomadic Arabs goes by the name of *gogué* in northern Nigeria, *masenqo* in Ethiopia, *gusle* in Yugoslavia, *er-hu* in China, *ghichak* in Afghanistan and *kijak* in Kirghizstan and so on.

Fortunately, there are occasional instances in which a name, or a variant of it, will always refer to the same type of instrument, even where thousands of miles separate them. Double reed instruments with a conical bore are most often called a variant of *surnai*, or *sirnai*, *sarune*, *shanai*, etc. This is not to say that other names are not used, such as the classical Arab *mizmar*, the *algaita* of Niger, the *gaida* of Yugoslavia, the *gaita* of Spain—manifestly all with the same root—or *zukra* in Arabia. These names, incidentally, are often used interchangeably for the reed instrument itself or when a bag has been added to produce a bagpipe.

The word *naqqara* is another term which refers only to one type of instrument: a pair of kettledrums usually of different sizes. Nakers is the English term, *nacaires* the French one, for these drums, along with their names, reached Europe during the Crusades. Similarly, *darabuka* refers only to a goblet-shaped single membrane drum, and *karna* to a long straight trumpet (now sometimes sawn off so that a double-reed mouthpiece can be used to facilitate playing). But specific names for widely-disseminated instruments are the exception rather than the rule.

Thus, what with the same or similar names referring to very different instruments, and the same instrument going by many and varied names, the best rule to follow would seem to be: don't trust a name unless you know precisely where the instrument comes from, and who plays it. Even the type of music may change an instrument's name, as we do, calling the classical violin a fiddle when a folk musician plays the same instrument. If we use the local name for a particular instrument in a particular place we can be reasonably accurate.

Reciting verses of the Qur'ān in Baghdad, with hand cupped behind the ear for resonance.

Classical Music

Arab Classical Music

Classical Arabic music was born in the seventh and eighth centuries at the courts of the *khalifs* in Al-Medīna, Damascus and Baghdad. Singers from various parts of the young Islamic world, attracted to these spiritual centres, took with them their local musical traditions and little by little a new music emerged, music which shows the influence not only of the Arabian peninsula, but of Persia, Syria and Byzantium as well. The philosophers of the time examined this music in the light of the ancient Greek theories with which they had become acquainted through the many valuable Arabic translations of Greek writers. The golden age of Islam (eighth to tenth centuries) is considered the golden age of classical Arabic music. From many sources, but primarily from the famous *Kitāb al-aghānī* (the Book of Songs) by Alī al-Isfahānī (897–967), we know of a considerable number of great Baghdad musicians like Tuwais, Ma'bad, Ibn Jāmi', Ibrahim al-Mausili, Ishaq al-Mausili, and Zalzal, to name only a few. One of these eminent musicians, Ziryāb, aroused the jealousy of Ishaq al-Mausili and was forced into exile. He went to the Maghreb but ended up in Al-Andalus (Spain) and became the father of the 'Andalusian' or 'Hispano-Arabic' music. The Arab Empire came to an end with the Mongol capture of Baghdad in 1258 and with the slow withdrawal of the Arabs from Al-Andalus (the last strongholds were abandoned in 1492). The next centuries are considered 'dark' centuries. We are quite remarkably ignorant of what may have happened in the field of music and it is the general conviction that the classical music of the Arabs was in decline, although a reviving inspiration from the new masters of the region, the Turks, may have been at work. In any case classical music survived, and in this century we are witnessing a renaissance of the great ancient traditions, though we do not know if it will be strong enough to resist the dangerous influences from the occident. At least there is now a sincere desire for a truly Arab identity in the field of music.

If we consider the classical music of today we discover easily that in the Arab world, just as in the Indian or western world, there are many local, slightly differing traditions of musical form, terminology, and instruments. But basically classical Arab music has two faces, an eastern and a western (this last covering only the Maghreb and its cultural dependencies).

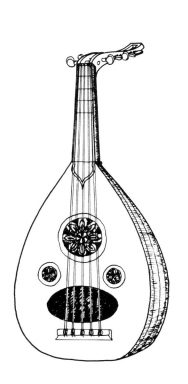

'Ud **A1.**

Rabāb and bow **A3.**

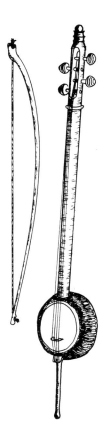

Jozé **A4.**

Three instruments are accepted everywhere in the Arab world as the main instruments of classical music: the lute *'ud* **A1**, the zither *qanun* **A2** and the oblique end-blown flute, *nay* **A7**.

Other instruments commonly used in classical music are the *kamān* or *kamāncha*; a fiddle **B3**—*kamān* being the Persian word for bow — in most areas today identical with the European violin, the *jozé* of Iraq (a four stringed spike fiddle with a coconut shell as a resonator) **A4**, the *kuitra* **G2** and the *rabāb* **A3** of the Maghreb. Several kinds of drums may be used for rhythmic accompaniment. Most common are the *darabuka* (goblet drum with one skin) **A5** and the *duff* (frame drum with cymbals inserted in the wooden frame) **A6**, but in the Gulf the *muruas* (little cylindrical two-skin drum of Sudanese or Nubian origin) **P2** is used to provide the rhythm for some of the songs with *'ud* accompaniment.

Classical Arabic music is basically a vocal art and in ancient times the normal word for music was *ghina* which means song. But even if the rhythmically structured pieces of music ordinarily demand a singer, melody-instruments may often be used for a non-metrical *taqsim* played as an introduction to a song, as an interlude or as a solo piece. The vocal counterpart of a *taqsim* is the *layāli*. If the *taqsim* is used as an introduction it is followed by a metrical and therefore drum-accompanied song, but (at least in Iraq and in the Gulf) a song in free rhythm may be introduced in between.

The Maghreb has been, and to some extent continues to be, famous for its *nauba*, musical suites in five or more movements, but *nauba* has been known in other parts of the Arab world as well. From Andalusian music the Arab world has furthermore acquired two poetic song forms, which are still held in high esteem: the *zajal* and the *muwashshah*.

All classical music is sung or played in a *maqām* or musical mode, and all rhythmic accompaniment follows strict rules, or rhythmic modes, the *iqa'at*.

Arabic music is performed by a soloist or by a small number of musicians. The ornamental style, well known from the architecture and decorative arts of the Arabs, may also be very pronounced in their music. Even if many traditional rules have to be followed by the master musician, his singing or playing will nevertheless be improvisatory. This refined art originally belonged to the courts and to the private houses of the rich and later on perhaps to the friendly gatherings of the connoisseurs but it has now entered the concert halls, not only of the Middle East, but of the whole world.

Instruments used in Arab Classical Music

A1 *'Ud*. Short lute. Damascus, Syria. L: 74 cm
A2 *Qanun*. Zither. Algiers, Algeria. L: 99 cm
A3 *Rabāb*. Fiddle. Fez, Morocco. L: 56 cm
A4 *Jozé*. Spike fiddle. Baghdad, Iraq. L: 66 cm
A5 *Darabuka*. Goblet drum. Damascus, Syria. L: 40 cm
A6 *Duff*. Frame drum. Damascus, Syria. L: 22·5 cm
A7 *Nay*. End-blown flute. Djelfa, Algeria. L: 41·5 cm

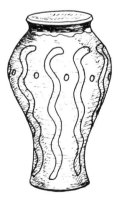

Nay **A7.**   *Duf* **A6.**   *Darabuka* **A5.**

Persian Classical Music

The classical music of contemporary Iran has its roots in the court music of the powerful Persia of antiquity. Unfortunately, our knowledge of this ancient music is almost non-existent. It is only from the period of the Sassanian empire (third to seventh century A.D.) that more precise information can be gleaned, telling us of famous musicians, such as the brilliant Barbad, court musician to Khosros II (king 590–628), and in general giving the impression that musical life at the courts of the time was refined and rich. There is no doubt that Persian music played an important role when, after the great Arabian conquests of the seventh and eighth centuries, the rich music of the Islamic Golden Age was developed at the courts of the *khalifs* in Damascus and Baghdad. But we must assume that the Persians, in the course of time, also received inspiration from the Arabs, which is indicated by the use in Persia of a musical terminology employing quite a number of Arabic words.

The classical music of present-day Iran has a character all of its own. This is clearly demonstrated by the instruments in use. The two most prominent stringed instruments are the *tar* and the *sehtar*, both words being of Persian origin, meaning 'string' and 'three strings' respectively. The *ṭar* **B1** is a double-bellied long-necked lute with six strings and is played with a small metal plectrum. It is used mainly as a solo instrument, but also to accompany singers.

The *sehtar* **B6** is a smaller instrument. Like the *tar* it is a long-necked lute, but its body is pear-shaped and it has only four strings. Its delicate tone makes it appropriate for intimate settings and in general it is heard as a solo instrument and only rarely in company with others.

The *santur* **B2** is a dulcimer, that is a zither the strings of which are played with sticks or hammers. The *santur* normally has eighteen groups of four strings tuned in unison and a range of two and a half octaves. Of equal importance in classical music is the *nay* **B5**, the end-blown flute made from a long piece of cane. Instruments of essentially the same structure and with the same (Persian) name are known in Arab countries and in Turkey, but each country's playing technique has its own peculiarities. The Persian *nay* player does not use a lip rest as his Turkish colleague would do, and while the Arab musician would press the aperture against his lips, the Persian will often press it against his teeth.

The spike-fiddle *kamāncha* **B3** belongs to the same family of instruments as the Iraqi *jozé* **A4**. It usually has four strings today, but in the provinces it may have three.

The normal drum for classical music is the *zarb* or *dombak* **B4**, a goblet drum, which in the Arab world would have been called *darabuka* or *tabla*.

Tar **B1.**

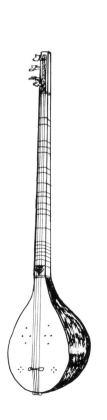

Sehtar **B6.**

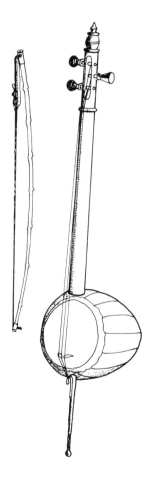

Kamāncha **B3.**

Persian classical music is played and sung at intimate gatherings; it is mainly improvised within a given mode and more or less closely follows a traditional formal scheme. There are seven main modes, called *dastgah*, and five auxiliary modes, called *avaz*. Each *dastgah* or *avaz* has its special repertory of melodic ideas, called *gusheh* and it is the task of the classical performer to present a number of *gusheh* in a reasonable order. Among the characteristics of Persian music is a pronounced predilection for ornamentation of a most subtle kind, which in the vocal music may include a combination of trilling and changes of register. Until recently rhythm had been of only secondary importance in this intimate music, but lately rhythm has gained in importance, partly due to the effect on the younger generation of western rock music, and partly due to the fact that Iran can count a virtuoso *zarb* player—Hossein Tehrani—among its foremost living musicians.

The music of the Sufis or dervishes has a considerable importance in Iran. This music is a prayer and a means of inducing a state of ecstasy. When performed by a group, it may include not only the singing and rhythmical breathing of the name of Allah, but the playing of instruments as well. Most commonly played are the *tambur* **F3**, a long-necked lute with two or three strings, the *sehtar* **B6**, the *nay* **B5** and the *duff* **P10**, but stringed instruments such as the *tar* **B1** and the *kamāncha* **B3** may occasionally be used as well.

The *zurkhane* (house of force) is nowadays a unique Persian phenomenon, dedicated to the performing of special physical exercises. Here the singers who direct the exercises sing old poems in praise of God, ordinarily in the mode of *Chahargah* with rhythmic accompaniment on a goblet drum considerably larger than the everyday *zarb*, which reverberates in the tiled gymnasium.

Zarb **B4**.

Instruments used in Persian Classical Music

B1   *Tar*. Long lute. Teheran, Iran. L: 93 cm
B2   *Santur*. Dulcimer. Teheran, Iran. L: 93 cm
B3   *Kamāncha*. Spike fiddle. Rezaiyeh, Iran. L: 94·5 cm
B4   *Zarb*. Goblet drum, 18th century. Teheran, Iran. L: 45·5 cm
B5   *Nay*. End-blown flute. Isfahan, Iran. L: 63·5 cm
B6   *Sehtar*. Long lute. Teheran, Iran. L: 76 cm
B7   *'Ud*. Short lute. Teheran, Iran. L: 74cm

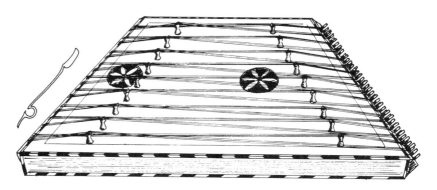

Nay **B5**.

Santur **B2**, and one of the beaters.

Turkish Classical Music

The classical forms of music from the different areas of the Middle East clearly belong to the same artistic family. Over the centuries there has been a continuous give-and-take between Persians, Arabs and Turks. It is undeniable that the classical Turkish music of today has been influenced by what is generally considered the traditional music of the Arabs. But it must be stressed that this influence worked the other way round as well. It should not be forgotten that the eminent philosopher and music theorist, the 'second master' (Aristotle being the first) Al Farabi (872–950) was a Turk. Of even greater importance is the fact that the major part of the Middle East, from the beginning of the fourteenth century and until quite recently, was dominated by the Osmanic Turks, whose Empire, at its height in the sixteenth century, stretched from the frontiers of Austria and southern Russia to India, from Morocco to the Arabian peninsula. Turkish musical ideas were widely spread during this long period.

The classical music has probably been influenced by the music of the mevlevi, or dervish brotherhoods, whose gatherings always used music as their main means of attaining a state of trance. The best singers took part in the ceremonies and several instruments could be used, primarily the flute *nay* **C3** and the framedrum *def* **P10** or the pair of kettledrums called *nakkare* or *kudum* **O3**. The imperial military bands (*mehterhane*), were also important although only a few of their instruments ever found their way into classical music.

The classical music of today employs the human voice and a limited number of instruments. Most prominent among the latter is the *'ud* **C5**, but the *nay* **C3** and the *kanun* **C4** are both represented by admirable musicians, while the *santur*, though worthy of mention, is of less importance. If all these instruments are also well known in other countries of the Middle East, there are nevertheless two which should nowadays be considered exclusively Turkish: the long-necked lute, *tanbur* **C1** and a special kind of fiddle called *kemençe* **C2**. A harp, *çeng* with twenty-four strings, was played until the eighteenth century. Foremost among the drums is the *deblek* or *darabuka* **C6**.

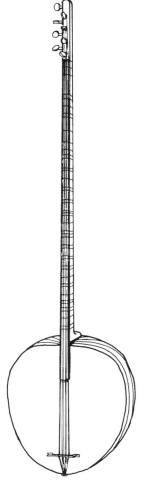

Tanbur **C1**.

As in other parts of the Middle East, classical music in Turkey is performed either by a soloist or by a small group of musicians. In the latter case they sing or play the same melody, but each in his individual way, thus creating the phenomenon which European scholars have called heterophony.

Classical music is composed or improvised in a *makam* and in this way belongs to the modal system of the whole of the Middle East. The rhythms are linked up with the system of rhythmic modes, *'usul*. The practice of music quite often involves rhythms of a remarkable sophistication and metres combining rhythmical units of two and three are favoured.

Among the instrumental forms still in vogue are the high classical *taksim* and the simpler *peşrev*, both of them typical kinds of preludes or interludes, and a popular form of rhythmical vocal music is *beste*. But music may also belong to a greater structure (*fasil*), with several movements or independent parts, such as a suite of the following movements (all sung or played in the same *makam*): *peşrev, kār, beste, ağirsemai, sarki, yürük semai, saz semai*, the first and last part being purely instrumental.

Turkish music is mainly improvised, but the names of many composers of traditional music from the past are still remembered, the most ancient being Hatip Zâkirî Hasan Efendi, who lived from 1545 to 1623. The use of the letters of the alphabet for the notation of music has been known since the time of Safieddin (Safi al-Din) in the thirteenth century but rarely practised. At the beginning of the nineteenth century an Armenian church musician, Hamparsum Limonciyan brought out a new kind of notation known as the *Hamparsum notasi*, which for some time was accepted by many musicians. Today a slightly altered version of European staff notation is used when notation is thought necessary or helpful.

Kemençe **C2.**

Instruments used in Turkish Classical Music

C1   *Tanbur*. Long lute. Istanbul, Turkey. L: 141 cm

C2   *Kemençe*. Fiddle. Ankara, Turkey. L: 38 cm

C3   *Nay*. End-blown flute with lip rest. Istanbul, Turkey. L: 73 cm

C4   *Kanun*. Zither L: 96 cm, with accessories for making, tuning, and playing the *kanun*. Ankara, Turkey.

C5   *'Ud*. Short lute. Aleppo, Syria. L: 74 cm

C6   *Darabuka*. Goblet drum. Aleppo, Syria. L: 31 cm

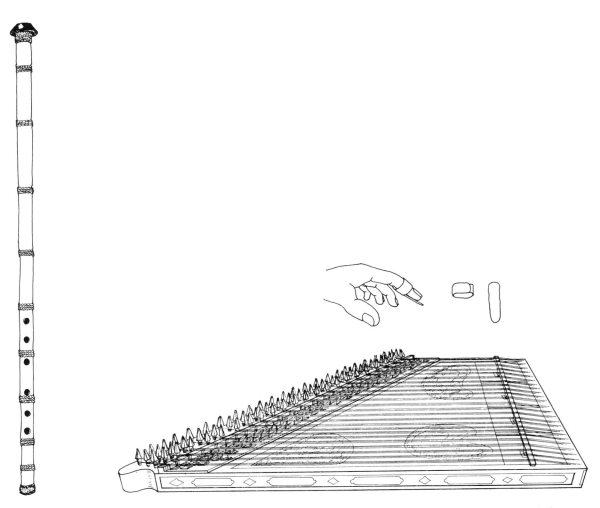

Nay with lip rest **C3**.

Kanun **C4**, and plectrum.

North Indian Classical Music

Middle Eastern and Central Asian influences are noticeable in some of the music from the Indian subcontinent, but it is not always easy to detect with absolute certainty the degree of this influence or the routes it has followed. Certainly Islamic inspiration was particularly strong during the reign of the Great Moghuls (fifteenth to eighteenth centuries), but it was at work even earlier. Amir Khusro (1254–1324) is considered one of the great musicians of ancient India, and he was at the same time a key figure in the spread of Persian musical feeling, and may well have been the inventor of the Islamic inspired *khyal*, today the most beloved of classical song genres. The Islamic influence gave a new colour to the musical traditions of what is now Pakistan and North India, and it is mainly due to this influence that the music of the north and of the south nowadays represent diverging emotional and technical styles. The power of the Muslim princes in the north never really extended to the southern part of the subcontinent.

Fundamentally North Indian music is a vocal music. For an instrumentalist the natural point of departure must always be the traditional style of singing. Several terms in vocal music are derived from Arabic or Persian sources. This is the case of the classical term *khyal*, and also for instance of the *tarāna*, where the term was introduced from Persia while some of the apparently 'meaningless' text-words used are Arabic (*yalāli* is an example of this), and of the popular genre *ghazal* : an Arabic word for love songs.

When we enter the field of musical instruments the relationship to the Middle East becomes even more evident, for many of the names are of Arabic or Persian origin. The *shahnāy* **M7**, a folk instrument which thanks to the distinguished art of Bismillah Khan became accepted in the world of classical music, is the local variant of the oboe known everywhere in the Islamic countries and usually by a variant of its Persian name *surnay*. It may be open to discussion whether or not the long-necked lute with six or seven strings and a considerable number of sympathetic strings, called *sitar* **D6**, originally came to the

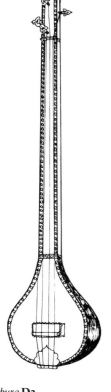

Tambura **D2**.

Indian subcontinent from Persia in a simpler form, but the name is purely Persian—meaning three strings—and is still used to denote one of the classical Persian instruments. *Rabāb* is a Persian word meaning many different stringed instruments of the Middle East, but primarily fiddles. In Pakistan and North India it has been used as the name for at least two kinds of short-necked lutes, one of them being almost identical to the *rubāb* **G5** of present day Afghanistan. Insofar as drums are concerned, in modern times the pair of drums *tabla* and *baya* **D1 & 1a** is by far the most commonly heard (used for all kinds of classical and semiclassical music with the exception of *dhrupad* and *dhamar*). *Tabla* is the Arabic word for drums in general, but here again the origin of the word does not necessarily indicate the origin of the instrument in question.

The ordinary North Indian music performance has a soloist who may be either a singer or an instrumentalist. The soloist needs at least a couple of assistants, the most important being the drum-player and one or more musicians who provide a continuous drone. If the soloist is a *shahnāy* player, the drone-playing may be entrusted to one or two other *shahnāy* players, but in most other cases the drone is produced by the long-necked lute with four open strings, called *tambura* **D2**, often reinforced by the little harmonium *surpeti* **D8**. This is certainly not Islamic. but a token of the influence from Christian missionaries in the nineteenth century. However, other accompanists may be included. This is especially common for singer–soloists, at the side of whom we may find either a player of the *sarangi* **D5** (a fiddle which at these occasions is highly regarded as its sonority resembles that of the

Sitar **D6.**

Tabla and *baya* **D1** and **1a.**

human voice), or another singer. A *sitar* player may be assisted by one or two other *sitar* players. In any case the main task of an assistant will be to imitate and occasionally to develop the musical phrases presented by the soloist in the intervals.

The classical music of Pakistan and North India is modal, following melodic modes called *raga* and rhythmic modes called *tala*. In instrumental music it is customary to start with a long *alapa* in free rhythm where the soloist in improvisation is exploring the chosen *raga* and expressing its particular mood. Then the drums begin and the soloist presents a fixed composition (*gat*) to which he returns quite frequently, but in between he allows his imagination to develop such improvisations as his mood and musicianship permit. Vocal music has many different forms but only a few of them allow for a long improvised introduction in free rhythm.

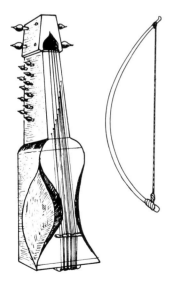

Sarangi **D5**.

Instruments used in North Indian Classical Music

D1 *Tabla* and *baya*. Pair of kettledrums. Lucknow,
& 1a India. L: 29 cm and L: 26·5 cm
D2 *Tambura*. Long lute used as a string drone. North India. L: 95 cm
D3 *Esraj*. Fiddle. Jaipur, India. L: 79 cm
D4 *Delruba*. Fiddle. Pakistan (bought in Kabul). L: 94 cm
D5 *Sarangi*. Short fiddle. Pakistan (bought in Kabul). L: 69 cm
D6 *Sitar*. Long lute. Lucknow, India. L: 136 cm
D7 *Rabob*. 19th century predecessor of the *sarod* used today in Indian classical music. North-west India. L: 80 cm
D8 *Surpeti*. 4 note drone harmonium. Lucknow, India. L: 33 cm

The Instruments and their History

Lutes

Long Lutes

Long lutes vary more in size, shape, name and function than any other type of instrument. More than four thousand years ago we find these instruments with a body and a long thin neck from Sumer and then Babylon and Egypt, and seals, plaques, figurines and tomb paintings show us how they were played. They are, in fact, the ancestors of most stringed instruments.

In form long lutes may still have the small bodies and long thin necks which pierce the soundbox of the ancient ones. They may be unfretted, but more commonly have frets which may be fixed or moveable, and are sometimes raised; the neck may be narrow or wide; the resonator may be round or oval, flat or deep or bulbous; the sound-board may be of wood or skin; the strings, which vary widely in number, may be fixed with a leather thong or, more frequently, with either rear or side pegs. Some are tiny, while others have necks almost as long as the player's arm, and he may use his fingers or a plectrum to pluck or strike either gut or wire strings.

This enormous diversity of form is rivalled by that of the names of the instruments. *Tanbur, tambur* and *pandur* are very common names for long lutes. *Tar,* an Iranian word for string, is often combined with numbers, so that we find *dutar* or *dotar* (two strings), *sehtar* or *sitar* (three strings) or *panchtar* (five strings). Thus considerable confusion results as regards more recent instruments: an Indian *sitar* **E8** and **D6** (which, despite the name, may have seven strings) is very different in sound, appearance

Long lute with pierced body from an Egyptian tomb painting.

Method of fastening the strings on ancient Egyptian long lutes, still in use in Niger today.

Colascione.

and playing techniques from a Persian *sehtar* **B6** (with four strings). The Afghan *tambur* **F5**, with its wide neck, moveable frets and sympathetic strings differs greatly from the Kurdish *tambur* **F3** with its small body and thin neck, and neither seems to bear much relation to the Turkish *tanbur* **C1**, with its large round body and enormously long thin neck, or to the *dombra* of the nomadic Kazakhs. The unfretted *dambura* **E1, 2, 3, 4** of the Afghan–Pakistani border is more of a rythmic than melodic instrument, while the unfretted Indian *tambura* **D2** serves only as a string drone with its four unfingered strings plucked in rapid succession to accompany a singer or solo instrument. Naturally enough, people from different language groups give their own names to the same types of long lutes, so that we find for instance, the *dutar* **E6** of Afghanistan, the *colascione* of Italy and the *dombra* of Kazakhstan all referring to a basically similar instrument. On the other hand, lutes with similar names may differ, such as the folk *gunbri* **F7** of Marrakesh, the *gunibri* or *suissen* **F8** used in the classical music of north Morocco and the ballad singer's *gurumi* of Niger. Various instruments of Central Asian origins migrated eastwards and the Chinese, the Mongolians, the Thais and the Vietnamese have all given different names to the similar long lutes which have further evolved in their own countries.

Finally, long lutes are notable in another aspect: they are used in art music, folk music, 'pop' commercial music and even in religious music. In general, instruments are used for one, or at most, two of these genres, but the great family of long lutes is an exception to this. In Turkey, for example, the *tanbur* is used only for classical music, but the *saz* or *baǧlama*, a different long lute, is a folk and also a pop music instrument. In India the *sitar* and *tambura* are instruments of classical music, as are the Persian *tar* and *sehtar*. On the other hand, the *saz* of Armenia and Azerbaijan is used by professional ballad singers, as is the *dombra* of the Kazakh and Kirghiz bards, and the *gunibri* and *gurumi* of the Saharan castes of professional musicians. Insofar as pop music is concerned, the Lebanese *buzuk*, the Greek *buzouki* and the Yugoslav *tamburitsa* are heard in films, on the radio and in night clubs, played by pop groups. Although the drum is the customary instrument used to induce trance, some Kurdish sects use their long lute, the *tambur*, for this purpose.

Thus long lutes, which originated in Persia and spread from there to so many parts of the world, are one of the oldest, most varied, versatile, and numerous of all groups of instruments found within the Islamic world.

Long Lutes

E1,2   *Dambura* (or *Danbore*). Unfretted lutes (showing
3, 4   differing styles, sizes and decoration). Eastern Afghanistan. L: 87·5 cm; 69·5 cm; 103·5 cm; 95·5 cm

E5   *Baglama* (or *saz*). Fretted lute. Ankara, Turkey. L: 124·5 cm

E6   *Dutar* (or *Dotar*). Long lute with frets and sympathetic strings. Herat, Afghanistan. L: 106 cm

E7   *Setar*. Fretted lute. Kabul, Afghanistan. L: 130 cm

E8   *Sitar*. Long lute with raised movable frets used in classical music. Pakistan (bought in Kabul). L: 121·5 cm

E9   Woodcarving of a woman playing a long lute. India. L: 42 cm

F1   *Chotara*. Long lute used as rhythmic string drone. Jaisalmer, India. L: 109 cm

F2   *Buzuk*. Long fretted lute used for folk music. Damascus, Syria. L: 107.5 cm

F3   *Tambur*. Long fretted lute used by Al Haq sect for religious (trance) music. Sanandaj, Kurdistan, Iran. L: 79·5 cm

F4   *Saz*. The long lute of Azerbaijan and Armenian epic singers or *ashugs*. Khoy, Azerbaijan, Iran. L: 104 cm

F5   *Tambur*. Broad necked fretted lute with sympathetic strings. Kabul, Afghanistan. L: 106 cm

F6   *Kountigui*. Pierced lute (body of pilchard tin, skin covered). Sonrai people, near Niamey, Niger. L: 45 cm

F7   *Gunbri*. Pierced lute used by *gnaoua* folk groups. Marrakesh, Morocco. L: 97 cm

F8   *Suissen*. Classical lute. Fez, Morocco. L: 65 cm

Tambur **F5** (left), *dambura* **E1, 2, 3, 4** (centre), *duf* (right).
Local group of musicians. Aq Sha, Afghanistan.

Singer with *dutar* **E6**. Tashqurghan, Afghanistan.

Classical music: *sitar* **D6** and **E8** player, with rhythm provided by *tabla* and *baya* **D1** and **1a**. Karachi, Pakistan.

Baluchi musicians singing *sher*, accompanied on: *chang* **N15** jew's harp (left); *dambura* **E1-4**, long lute (next left and far right); *saroz* **I11**, waisted short fiddle. Quetta, Pakistan.

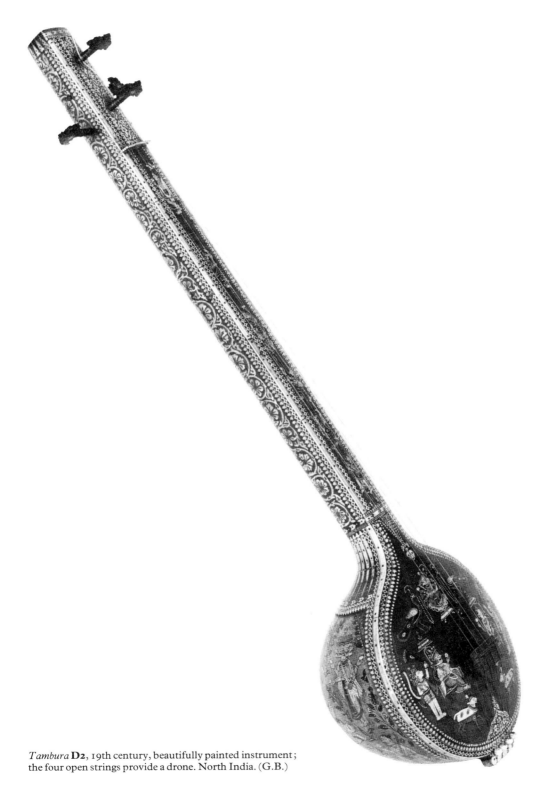

Tambura **D2**, 19th century, beautifully painted instrument;
the four open strings provide a drone. North India. (G.B.)

Tanbur **C1**, used in Turkish classical music. Istanbul, Turkey.

Saz **F4** maker, playing his own instrument. Azerbaijan, Iran.

Tambur **F3** used by the Al Haq sect to achieve ecstasy. Kurdistan, Iran.

Gunbri **F7**, used for accompaniment by a group of local musicians. Marrakesh, Morocco.

Suissen **F8**, used in classical music. Fez, Morocco.

The *gurumi* accompanies the
ballads. Dosso, Niger.

The long lutes with a barb are called Kashgar *rubāb* and the small frame drums with jingles are *daira*. Uighur people, Sinkiang,
South-west China.

A stone rubbing on a rice paper shows a musical scene in Thailand, the *saw sam sai* or spike fiddle; the *grajappi* or long lute the *thon* or goblet drum. Obtained in Bangkok, Thailand. (G.B.)

Short Lutes

Representations of the pear-shaped lute, hollowed out of a single block of wood, with the body tapering to form the neck and pegbox, are found in many parts of Central Asia from about two thousand years ago (although one example from the eighth century B.C. in Persia is known). Samarkand figurines, the Airtam frieze from Soviet Central Asia, Gandhara statuettes, Chinese Turkestani frescos all show the same type of lute, which spread into the centres of Arabic culture to become the greatest instrument of Arabic classical music.

By the ninth century there were a number of treatises on music from both practical and theoretical points of view, and all musical theory was made to conform to the *'ud* with its four pairs of strings. Before the end of that century most of the ancient Greek treatises on music and mathematics were translated into Arabic, causing a great increase of interest in music, and particularly in the *'ud*. The *'ud* was used for solo instrumental music—a *taqsim*—as well as to accompany a singer. It went with the Moors into Spain, where it acquired a fifth pair of strings. Rather interestingly the *'ud* of the Maghreb today **G1** usually has only four pairs while that of Syria, Egypt and Iraq uses the five **A1** and occasionally a sixth single string is added. Today it can be heard in all Arabic and Turkish classical music, and it is used for much traditional music as well. Played with an eagle's quill plectrum, its tone is resonant, the melody clear, and its players held in the highest esteem accorded to musicians.

Another noteworthy group of short lutes exists: the deep, waisted lutes with skin bellies and sympathetic strings. The Afghan *rubab* **G4**, the Indian and Pakistani *rabob* **D7** and the modern Indian *sarod* all belong to this group, and are used for both traditional and classical music. The Persian *tar* was of this type originally, but its neck has been lengthened so that it now belongs to the long lutes. Nevertheless, its body betrays its recent history. It is used for classical music only, and is very prominent in modern ensembles in Iran.

Short Lutes

G1   *'Ud.* Lute with four courses of strings, used in Andalusian classical music. Fez, Morocco. L: 89 cm

G2   *Kuitra.* Small version of the Andalusian classical *'ud.* Algiers, Algeria. L: 87·5 cm

G3   *Mandole.* Lute with longer neck used in traditional music. Algiers, Algeria. L: 97 cm

G4   *Rubāb.* Waisted lute used in traditional music. Kabul, Afghanistan. L: 64 cm

G5   *Rubāb.* Short lute. Kabul, Afghanistan. L: 86 cm

G6   *Tar.* Shown here to demonstrate how the neck of a short waisted lute lengthens into a long lute. Teheran, Iran. L: 94 cm

G7   *'Ud* (or *rubāb* or *qobuz*). Folding model. Ṣan'ā', Yemen Arab Republic. L: 80·5 cm

Kuitra **G2** (left), Andalusian short lute with four pairs of strings. *Gunibri* (right), long lute. Fez, Morocco.

Rubāb **G4**. Waisted short lute with deep body, used for traditional music. Kabul, Afghanistan (G.B.)

'*Ud* **A1**. The classical Arab lute. Baghdad, Iraq.

Sarod. The modern descendant of the *rabob*, used as a solo instrument in North Indian classical music. Karachi, Pakistan.

Rabob. Singer accompanying himself in traditional music. Peshawar, Pakistan.

Fiddles

Fiddles are lutes whose strings are bowed, and, as with plucked lutes, fiddles fall into two main types. From the long lutes, whose thin necks pierce a small resonator, the spike fiddles are derived, while from the short, pear-shaped lutes come all the remaining fiddles and violins. Again, as with long lutes, the simple spike fiddles are more widely disseminated not only in the centre of the Islamic world, but from as disparate areas as northern Nigeria and Mali in one direction, to Tanzania and Ethiopia on the opposite coasts of Africa, through to China and Vietnam in the Far East, and Thailand, Malaysia and Java in South-east Asia.

It must be remembered that the art of bowing, which originated in the Islamic and Byzantine empires, is only about a thousand years old, and is thus comparatively recent insofar as the history of musical instruments is concerned. At about the tenth century, however, the expansion of Islam with the resultant cultural interchange and trade, was in a dynamic state, and bowed lutes—like so many other easily portable items—as well as new concepts (in this case the idea of causing the strings of a lute to sound by stroking them with an arched wooden bow with a horsehair string resined to increase the friction) were carried from the concentrations in the centres to the far distant areas of Africa and eastern Asia. The new technique was rapidly assimilated, and while fiddles occasionally replaced other local instruments, more frequently their long drawn-out notes were added either to existing folk or classical musical instruments.

Among the nomads of the desert the spike fiddle, called *rabāb* **H2**, was, and is, a folk instrument, used mainly to accompany epic poetry. It is also a folk instrument in East and West Africa: the *masenqo* **H8** of Ethiopia and the *godjie* **H5** of Niger show some of the variations in form and construction. In the developing classical music of the Arabs and Persians, however, the spike fiddle was used for a different repertoire and is an essential part of art music there to this day. The *jozé* **A4** of Baghdad and the *kamāncha* **B3** of Teheran are basic to the classical music in those cities, although today the bowed instrument is most often a European violin (this is a case of an instrument obtained from Islamic sources re-introduced in a different form into the area from which it originated). Another interesting use of the spike fiddle can be found in Java and Malaysia, where the *rabāb* **H11** is often heard leading the classical *gamelan* orchestra of metallophones, gongs and xylophones which has been traditional to the area for many centuries.

The short lute, originally hollowed out of one block of wood, resulted in a similar construction in its bowed equivalent. This is the classical *kemençe* **C2** of Turkey, with its derivatives the *lira* **I4** of Crete, the *gadulka* of Bulgaria and the *lyritsa* of Yugoslavia, all used in the present-day folk music of the Balkans. The Indian and Baluchi fiddles are also hollowed out of one piece of wood, but while the idea of bowing came from Islamic areas, as did the lutes themselves, bowing seems to have been practised first by the nomads of the steppes further north, the Kirghiz, Kazakhs and Mongolians, who transmitted the use of the bowed lute in a somewhat changed form to the Indian sub-continent. Certainly the short lutes and fiddles of North India, Pakistan, Kashmir and Afghanistan seem very different in shape from those further west. They are heavy instruments, generally barbed; the belly is often made of leather or parchment, and frequently the upper half of the soundbox is left open. The Indian *sarinda* **I7**, the Baluchi *saroz* **I10, 11** and **12** and the Nuristani fiddle **I8** all belong to this type; they are all used in folk music, or to accompany epic singing. The *sarangi* **I5**, on the other hand, is used mainly for classical music, although it too is made from a single piece of heavy wood.

As the construction of short lutes changed so that the body, neck and pegbox were made separately, so too did that of the short fiddles. The neck became narrower and usually longer, the body flattened and elongated and was made of thinner wood. The small Black Sea *kemençe* **I1** was undoubtedly a forerunner, possibly even a prototype, of the European fiddle of the early Middle Ages. Mersenne, writing in 1636, shows in great detail an instrument which is almost identical, and paintings and carvings as early as the thirteenth century show a variety of similar fiddles, usually played by angels. The new instruments evidently became very popular and many varieties developed in different areas. Our viol family as well as violins all have their origin in the Middle East. The classical *rabāb* **A3** of Morocco arrived in Spain before the fourteenth century, and it is only in the past few decades that the European violin (body held against the player's knee) has begun to replace the *rabāb* in the Andalusian music of Morocco and Algeria, as well as in the classical ensembles of Arab, Turkish and Iranian music. Even the spike fiddles are being ousted by the European violin, but the music remains the same.

Fiddles

H1 *Rabāb*. Spike fiddle. Nubia, Egypt. L: 95 cm
H2 *Rabāb*. Spike fiddle. Petra, Jordan. L: 72 cm
H3 *Ghichak*. Spike fiddle. Kabul, Afghanistan. L: 80 cm
H4 *Kamāncha*. Spike fiddle. Rezaiyeh, Iran. L: 70 cm
H5 *Godjie*. Spike fiddle. Zinder, Niger. L: 70 cm
H6 *Nanga*. Spike fiddle. Bukoba, Tanzania. L: 64 cm
H7 *Er-hu*. Spike fiddle. Peking, China. L: 50 cm
H8 *Masenqo*. Spike fiddle. Gondar, Ethiopia. L: 67 cm
H9 *Rabāb soussi*. Spike fiddle. Marrakesh, Morocco. L: 42 cm
H10 *Rāvaṇhattho*. Spike fiddle. Jodhpur, India. L: 85 cm
H11 *Rabāb*. Spike fiddle. Kota Baharu, Malaysia. L: 115 cm

I1 *Karadeniz kemençe*. Fiddle. Maçka, Turkey. L: 56 cm
I2 *Kemençe*. Classical fiddle. Ankara, Turkey. L: 50 cm
I3 *Keman*. Fiddle. Istanbul, Turkey. L: 60 cm
I4 *Lira*. Fiddle. Crete, Greece. L: 50 cm
I5 *Sarangi*. Classical fiddle. Lahore, Pakistan. L: 66 cm
I6 *Sindhi sarangi*. Folk fiddle. Jaisalmer, India. L: 66 cm
I7 *Sarinda*. Fiddle. Lucknow, India. L: 63 cm
I8 *Sarang*. Fiddle. Nuristan, Afghanistan. L: 80·5 cm
I9 *Kemayche*. Fiddle. Jaisalmer, India. L: 73 cm
I10 *Saroz*. Fiddle. Kandahar, Afghanistan. L: 46.5 cm
I11 *Saroz*. Fiddle. Baluchistan, Afghanistan. L: 58·5 cm
I12 *Saroz*. Fiddle. Used by Baluchi people. Karachi, Pakistan. L: 62 cm

Man from the Panjshir Valley playing the *ghichak* **H3** he has made from a biscuit tin. Kabul, Afghanistan.

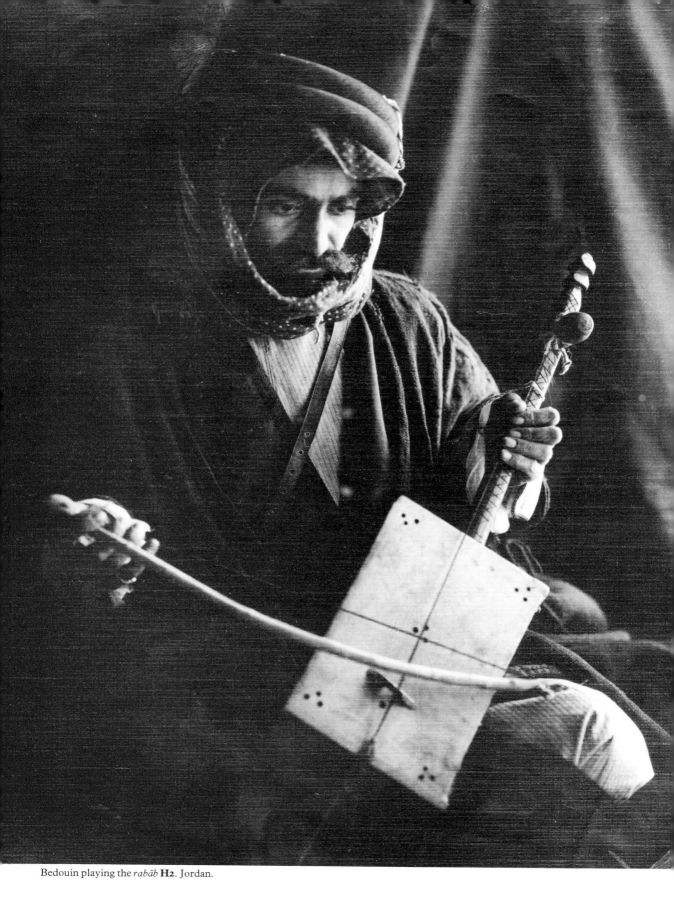

Bedouin playing the *rabāb* **H2**. Jordan.

The *jozé* **A4** or spike fiddle used in Arabic classical music. Baghdad, Iraq.

The Soussi *rabāb* **H9** which accompanies epics and ballads has one horsehair string which is played to the side of the neck, like the Indian *ravaṇhatto* **H10**. Marrakesh, Morocco.

The *masenqo* **H8**, one string spike fiddle which accompanies the 'wax and gold' music. Gondar, Ethiopia. (G.B.)

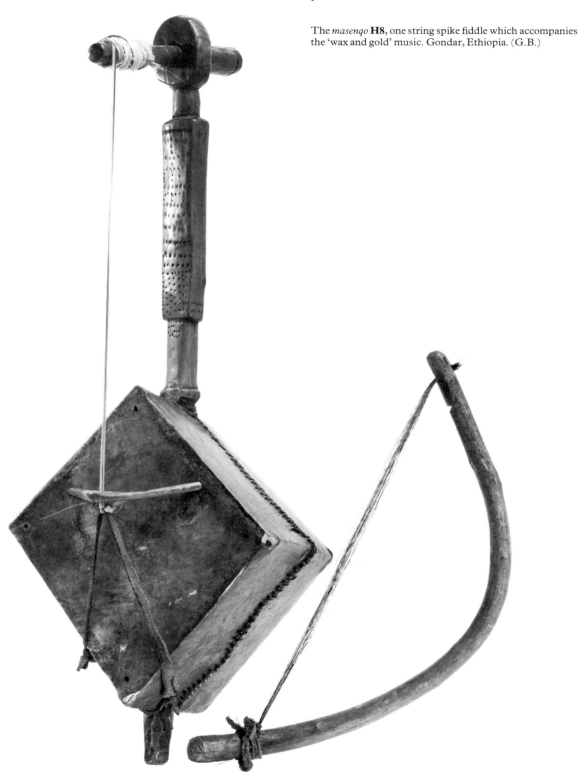

The *rabāb* **H11** and bow of South-east Asia take on the
graceful curves of that area. Kota Baharu, Malaysia. (G.B.)

The Raj Gonds of Adilibad have special bards who accompany themselves on this spike fiddle. Hyderabad, Deccan, India.

The Black Sea fiddle, or *karadeniz kemençe* **11** playing for a dance. Maçka, Turkey.

Detail of the carving of the *lira*. Crete, Greece. (G.

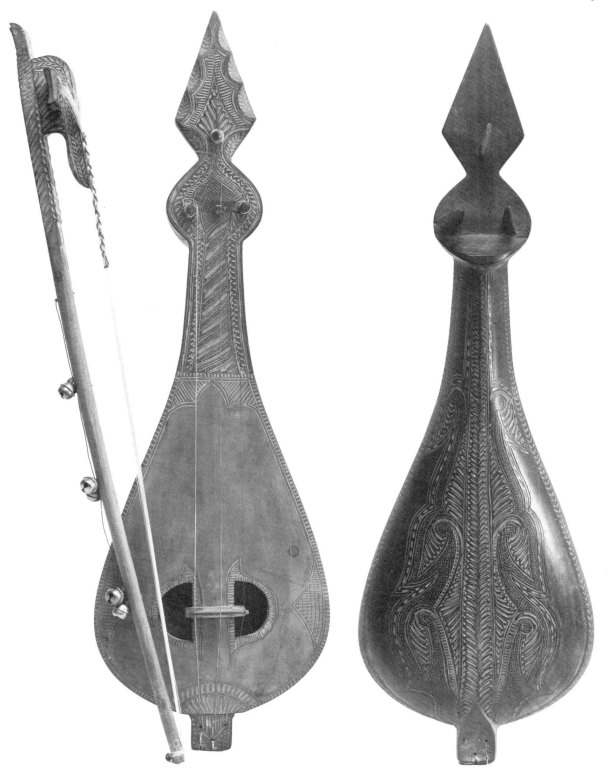

Lira I4, the folk fiddle from Crete. Crete, Greece. (G.B.)   Decoration on the back of the *lira*. Crete, Greece. (G.B.)   **47**

Kemayche **I9** (left), *dhol* (centre), *surnai* (right) playing Rajasthani folk music. Jaisalmer, India.

Ben Harbit making a classical
rabāb **A3**. Fez, Morocco.
(Marc Loopuyt)

Lyres, Harps and Zithers

Stringed frame instruments (that is, lyres and harps) appeared very early in the now Islamic parts of the world. We know of both the box lyre and the bowl lyre five thousand years ago in Ur (in Iraq) and from there they spread to Egypt and Greece. Today Ethiopia is the only country where the box lyre, *bagana* **J4** is still used, but this is an interesting case of social continuity since the Sumerian ones were obviously used by royalty of the time, being inlaid with silver and precious stones. Until the very recent past these instruments were used for Christian religious allegories by the royal family and nobility of Ethiopia, and only by them. The bowl lyre, on the other hand, has been the common people's instrument **J2**, used to accompany ballads and poetry. More recently, after the bowl lyre spread to Sudan (where it is usually called *tambura*) it was used in the *zar* cult to cast out the evil spirits causing disease and mental distress. Sudanese slaves have carried both the cult and its instruments to Eritrea, Arabia, Yemen, and the Gulf, and have even penetrated to Hyderabad in the Deccan (India). Unlike the instrument when it is used to accompany epics and love songs in Sudan and Eritrea, its use in the *zar* cult is more that of a rhythmic string instrument than a melody one **J1**.

Harps, whether arched or angular are also known to have existed at least five thousand years ago. Those found in the royal cemetery at Ur are complete and highly developed instruments, so it is reasonable to suppose that simpler forms existed long before then. They travelled from the centres of Mesopotamia to all urbanized areas of Asia and Africa, including Greece **J5**; later, with the spread of Islam they reached most of Nilotic Africa and the high mountain regions of Asia. Persian and Turkish miniatures show harps being played at feasts and festivities, in love scenes and even on horseback. By the eighteenth century, however, these harps had become extinct except in a few areas: there are folk harps in Africa as far south as Zaïre, and while most of them are bow harps at least a few in the centre of the Ituri Forest are angle harps. They are perhaps most common in Uganda. In Asia they

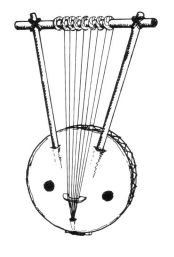

Bowl lyre.

continue to be used only in two quite dissimilar places: the *wuj* **J3** of Nuristan in Afghanistan is a primitive bow harp with four strings used in folk music, while in Burma the *soung* is a beautifully made and decorated instrument used in classical music.

The zither, whose numerous strings are stretched over one bridge at each end across the whole of the soundbox and running parallel to it, is a somewhat later arrival. We first know of it as a Phoenician instrument. It was rarely mentioned from then until the tenth century in Syria but was known to exist in both Egypt and Persia and its name, in an early story of the *Arabian Nights*, is the Arabic *qanun* **A2** and **C4**. Its gut strings are arranged in courses of three, stretched over a flat trapezoidal box and today ditals allow the player to tune these to quarter tones. A horn plectrum is fastened to both index fingers of the player by means of a ring. The tone is both soft and brilliant, and this is an instrument used only for Arab and Turkish classical music, for which it is eminently suited. The struck zither, or dulcimer, has been discussed in

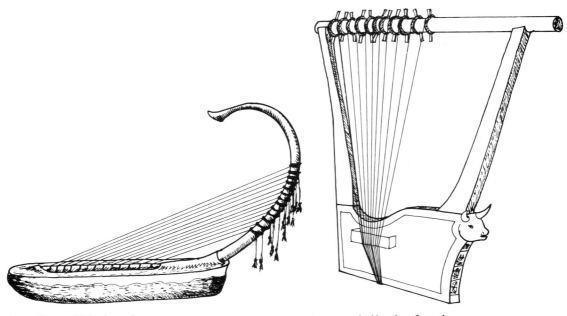

Arched harp with horizontal strings from Burma *(soung)*.

Asymmetrical box lyre from the royal tomb at Ur.

Persian classical music, but it does exist in Soviet Central Asia as well as in the Far East and Europe (see 'Islamic Influences on the Music of the World').

Lyres and Harps

J1 *Tambura*. Bowl lyre. Manama, Bahrain. L: 117 cm
J2 *Kerar*. Bowl lyre. Dessie, Ethiopia. L: 57 cm
J3 *Wuj*. Bow harp. Nuristan, Afghanistan. L: 46·5 cm
J4 Painting of *bagana* player 'David playing the harp' (which is a mis-translation of lyre). Gondar, Ethiopia. L: 25 cm
J5 Statuette showing a harp player, c. 500 B.C. Greece. L: 7·4 cm

Arched harp with vertical strings from Ancient Egypt.

Statuette showing an *aulos* **J4** (double reed pipes) player and a harpist. c. 500 BC, Greece. (G.B.)

The *kanun* **C4** is used for fine classical music (the Arabic term is *qanun*). Ankara, Turkey.

Sudanese musicians, formerly of the Nizam's orchestra, playing the *tambura* **J1** or large
lyre which is also played by Sudanese throughout the Gulf area. Hyderabad, Deccan, India.

Flutes

Unlike so many of the instruments discussed thus far, which have originated in the Islamic world, flutes would appear to have been 'invented' independently in many different regions. Stone age flutes have been discovered, preserved in Siberian ice, in English clay, in Danish and Irish peatbogs, in African and South American sands. Interestingly, most of these bone flutes are duct or whistle flutes, a somewhat complicated type which preceded by many millenia the flutes found in Islamic areas. The latter are end-blown flutes: a piece of bamboo with the top edge sharpened. The player blows across this edge while the long flute is held vertically or obliquely. From the point of view of construction this is the simplest of all flutes, but the *nay* **A7, B5, C3** and **K1–6**, as it is called by its Persian name throughout the Islamic world, (except in North-west Africa where the old Arabic word *qussaba* or *qasba* is used) is the most difficult of all to play. When the flutist is skillful the sound is of surpassing beauty. In classical Arab, Persian and Turkish music the *nay* is essential to all ensembles, and is a solo instrument as well. In both Turkey and the Maghreb it is also used for religious music by many of the dervish orders and brotherhoods where it has an important role in trance music. The *nay* is played with non-stop breathing throughout the Islamic world.

Other forms of flutes—the ancient duct flutes and the cross, or transverse horizontal flutes—are found in Islamic areas. The duct flutes **K7–10** tend to be shepherd's instruments, while the transverse flute **K11** developed to an art music instrument in India and China and is occasionally heard in Muslim countries such as Iran, Afghanistan and Central Asia. Double duct flutes—a pair held loosely in the player's mouth—are still used in Armenia and parts of Baluchistan and western India. Called *satara* in Pakistan **K8** the music they produce is extremely beautiful.

End-blown flutes

K1   *Nay*. End-blown flute. Djelfa, Algeria. L: 70·5 cm

K2   *Nay*. End-blown flute. Ankara, Turkey. L: 89 cm

K3   *Kaval*. End-blown flute. Rhodope Mountains, Bulgaria. L: 71 cm

K4   *Saréoua*. End-blown flute. Agadez, Niger. L: 46 cm

K5   *Nay*. End-blown flute. Isfahan, Iran. L: 54 cm

K6   *Nay*. End-blown flute for folk music. Khoy, Iran. L: 54·3 cm

Duct flutes

K7   *Kaval*. Duct flute. Maçka, Turkey. L: 54·5 cm

K8   *Satara* (pair). Duct flutes. Quetta, Pakistan. L: 56 cm

K9   *Nay* (bedouin). Duct flute. Eastern Syria. L: 35·5 cm

K10   *Kaval*. Duct flute. Aleppo, Syria. L: 32·5 cm

Transverse flute

K11   *Belever*. Transverse flute. Rezaiyeh, Iran. L: 33·5 cm

Trumpets

Trumpets—long, cylindrical instruments of metal—have been known in ancient Egypt, Greece and Rome and other Mediterranean areas ever since metal-working was commonly used in the area. Harsh sounding and often used with the raucous double-reed instruments and kettledrums, they produced military music which was loud, rhythmic and exciting. The *nafir* **K12** can be seen in Turkish, Persian and Moghul miniatures showing battle scenes, and undoubtedly the instrument was carried to Europe by soldiers returning from the Crusades. In the Maghreb it is used to signal the time of Ramadan; further south among the Hausa of Niger and Nigeria each sultan or emir has a court ensemble to welcome and entertain guests, and the two notes of the *kakaki* (which sometimes has a double bell to amplify the sound) **K14** are always heard there. In central Asia it is called *karna* or *karnay*; as it grew longer it was either carried with the bell across the shoulders of a young boy or an S-bend was made to shorten its length **Q7**. Eventually it was folded completely, as in the folk trumpets of Rajasthan **K15**.

In Europe two distinct styles of trumpet music evolved: the military trumpet (whose possession was restricted to the nobility) was a strong outdoor instrument with a limited range and low register as it has continued to be in the Islamic world, but a more brilliant orchestral trumpet and trombone had become part of the classical music scene in western Europe by the sixteenth century.

Trumpets

K12 *Nafir*. Trumpet. Fez, Morocco. L: 170 cm
K13 *Nafir*. Trumpet. Marrakesh, Morocco. L: 49 cm
K14 *Kakaki*. Trumpet with double bell. Konni, Niger. L: 200 cm
K15 *Bankia*. Folded folk trumpet. Jaipur, India. L: 86 cm

Kaval **K3**

Kaval **K3**, end-blown wooden flute, turned on a lathe.
Rhodope Mountains, Bulgaria. (G.B.)

Nay **K1**

Nay **K1**, end-blown flute of bamboo, made by a master and
two apprentices. Near Djelfa, Algeria. (G.B.)

Nay **K1** or classical end-blown flute. Fez, Morocco.

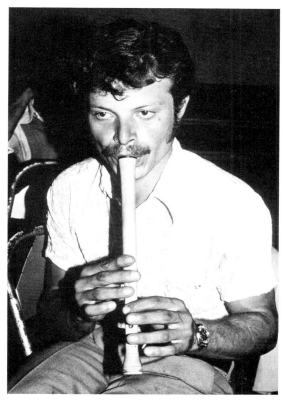

Kaval **K7**, duct flute used for folk songs. Maçka, Turkey.

Nay player. Kurdistan, Iran.

Single Reed Instruments—Clarinets

Throughout the whole of the Islamic world, cylindrical instruments with a single beating reed are to be found; and wherever else in the world they occur, they can all be traced to their Middle Eastern origins. These small cane instruments have a tongue slit three ways around in the upper end, and the whole reed is held inside the player's mouth. Non-stop breathing gives a continuous sound and the cylindrical tube produces a tone, softer and less shrill than that of an oboe, but more penetrating and resonant than that of a flute. These single reed instruments are almost always found in pairs, so that the Arabic term *zummara* refers to a double clarinet. The instrument is known from ancient Egypt and Assyria, and the simplest form seems identical to that used by the bedouins today **L1**. The names may vary: *zamr* in Morocco, *mizmar* or *mizwej* in Syria, *mutbej* in Iraq, *mazaamir* in Yemen, *dozale* in Kurdistan, *koshnai* in Uzbekistan, *çifte* in Turkey are some of the best-known. The form of all these is basically the same in that each of the pipes has the same number of fingerholes, and the player places the first three fingers of each hand across both pipes. The pipes are not tuned to an exact unison, but are just enough off to beat and thus to give an exciting sound.

The external form of these double clarinets can vary from extremely simple **L1, 2, 3, 4** to those where a horn bell amplifies the sound **L6**, and to those in which a bag or gourd has been added so that a larger wind reservoir than the player's cheeks can be obtained **L5 and 7**. The Egyptian *arghul* **L15** has one melody pipe and a long drone pipe, while the simpler Turkish *argun* **L12** has a drone of the same size as the melody pipe, and the *murli* **L13** of Rajasthan has unequal pipes and uses a gourd reservoir. Hornpipes form a third group: the pipes are of the same length, but not only is there a horn bell at the base, but the player often blows into a horn bell to activate the reeds, instead of keeping them in his mouth. The Basque *alboka* (the name is Arabic for 'the horn') is such an instrument, as is the Welsh *pibcorn*. Sometimes the horn is replaced by a wooden cradle as in the hornpipe from Crete **L9** and the bagpipes from the same island **L10**, which are similar to the *tulum* **L14** from Turkey.

Finally, there are a number of single clarinets. These simple instruments are sometimes idioglotic (that is, the reed is cut directly into the pipe with the fingerholes) as those found in Syria **L16**, Crete **L17** and amongst the Turkoman **L18**; sometimes the reeds are separate, and they may add a bell. As in flutes, here is a case in which the more complex—that is, the double clarinets—preceded the simpler single forms. Furthermore, the single clarinet (except for the modern European form, which does not derive from the Islamic clarinet) is seldom seen, while the double clarinets are spread throughout the whole of the Islamic world.

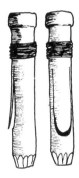

Reeds for double clarinet.

Angle harp from a 6th century Persian miniature.

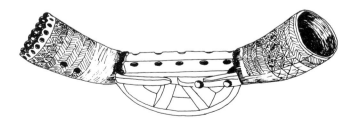

Alboka, Basque hornpipe.

Single Reed Instruments

L1   *Zummara*. Double clarinet. Petra, Jordan.
L: 31·5 cm

L2   *Mizmar*. Double clarinet. Aleppo, Syria.
L: 36 cm

L3   *Zummara*. Double clarinet c. 1850. Hyderabad, Deccan, India. L: 24 cm

L4   *Mazaamir*. Double clarinet. Zabeed, Yemen Arab Republic. L: 27 cm

L5   *Jirba*. Bagpipes. Manama, Bahrain. L: 86 cm

L6   *Zamr*. Double clarinet with horn bells.
Hammamet, Tunisia. L: 25 cm

L7   *Zukra*. Bagpipes. Tunis, Tunisia. L: 55 cm

L8   *Zamr*. Double clarinet with single horn bell.
Foum el Ançur, Morocco. L: 35 cm

L9   *Çifte*. Double hornpipe. Crete, Greece. L: 29 cm

L10 *Tsambouna*. Bagpipes. Crete, Greece. L: 80 cm

L11 *Tulum*. Bagpipes. Çamle Hemçin, Turkey.
L: 54 cm

L12 *Argun*. Double clarinet (with drone). Iskenderun, Turkey. L: 32 cm

L13 *Murli*. Gourd pipes (with drone). Borunda, Rajasthan, India. L: 44 cm

L14 *Tulum*. Bagpipes. Istanbul, Turkey. L: 54 cm

L15 *Arghul*. Double clarinet (with long drone). Faiyum, Egypt. L: 180 cm

L16 *Zumar*. Set of single clarinets. Aleppo, Syria.
L: 18·5 cm, 21·5 cm, 25·5 cm

L17 *Düduk*. Single idioglot clarinet. Crete, Greece.
L: 24·5 cm

L18 *Dil-tyuduk*. Single clarinet. Turkoman people, Daulatabad, Afghanistan. L: 27 cm

L19 *Düduk*. Single horn pipe. Crete, Greece. L: 27·5 cm

L20 *Gayda*. Bagpipes with drone. Rhodope Mountains, Bulgaria. L: 80 cm

Hausa musicians playing the *nafir* **K13**. Northern Nigeria.

The *jirba* **L5** (meaning 'bag'), played with drums at a feast in Manama, Bahrain. (P.R.O.)

The reeds of the *çifte* **L9**. Crete, Greece. (G.B.)

Zummara **L3** made of eagle's leg bones, and played by a member of the orchestra of the former Nizam of Hyderabad. The player's ancestors brought the instrument from the Hadramaut. Hyderabad, Deccan, India.

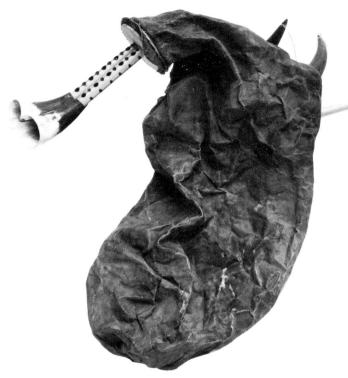

Zukra **L7**. Hammamet, Tunisia. (G.B.)

Çifte **L9**, a double hornpipe in a wooden cradle. Crete,
Greece. (G.B.)

Zamr **L8** player. Near Beni Mellal, Morocco.

Zamr **L6** with double horn bell. Hammamet, Tunisia. (G.B.)

A simple type of *tulum* **L14**. Bought in Istanbul, Turkey.

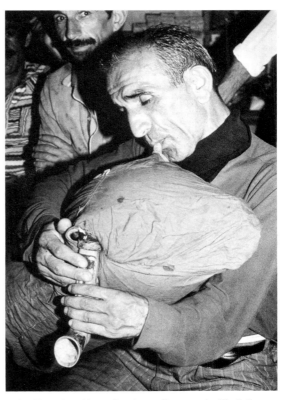

Tulum **L11** played by a piper in a valley near the Black Sea, Çamle Hemşin, Turkey.

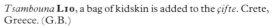

Tsambouna **L10**, a bag of kidskin is added to the *çifte*. Crete, Greece. (G.B.)

Playing the *argun* **L12**. One pipe gives a drone. Iskenderun, Turkey. (P.R.O.)

Dil-tyuduk **L18**. Turkoman people, Daulatabad, Afghanistan.

Düduk **L19**, single hornpipe. Crete, Greece. (G.B.)

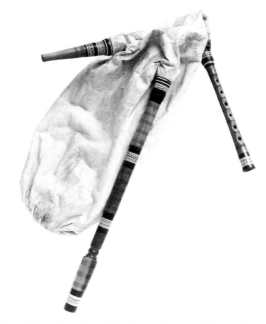

Gayda **L20**, bagpipes with a drone. Rhodope Mountains, Bulgaria. (G.B.)

Modern toy bagpipes, using balloons for the bag and a single reed chanter. Patna, India.

Double Reed Instruments—Shawms (Oboes)

Double reed instruments, frequently played in pairs, seem to have been fairly common in the ancient world of Mesopotamia, Arabia and Egypt almost five thousand years ago, although the softer wind instruments—vertical flutes and double clarinets—predominated. But in the era of loud, outdoor military music about a thousand years later, the double reed instruments came into their own, still more when the conical shawm appeared somewhat later and held its position in outdoor ensembles and military music (with or without a bag added) to the present day.

The reed of a shawm is made of two pieces of thin reed bound around a metal staple with thread; this is placed on a pirouette or lip-rest, circular in shape, and the whole is inserted into a lathe-turned wooden instrument, generally conical in bore. The sound is extremely raucous and penetrating, very well suited to military and processional music. It is an instrument found in all Islamic countries, often played with non-stop breathing. It gathers the wedding guests, welcomes visitors, marks the hours and leads the troops into battle.

The names of the conical shawm are generally some variant of *zurna, surnay, shahnāy, sona,* etc. Occasionally a totally different name is used, such as the *saz,* **M3** (meaning musical instrument in Turkish) of the Qashqai nomads of southern Iran. The same people use another larger shawm called *karna* **M6** but in this case the name gives the history of the instrument. *Karna* or *karnai* is the long trumpet of Central Asia and the Arabic lands but it is difficult to play or carry. So the Qashqai have cut off the bell of the trumpet and fastened it to a conical shawm and have continued to call the instrument *karna,* trumpet. The Chinese name for the conical shawm, *sona* **M10** also tells of its history, for it obviously derives from the *surnai* of Turkestan or India; the tiny *sarune* **M8** of the Batak peoples of Sumatra has the same origin.

Cylindrical oboes are much older than the louder conical ones, but they are much less frequently found. The music of the *balaban* **M11** of Kurdistan or the *mey*

M12 of Turkey or the *kwan* **M13** of China is soft indoor music, sounding more like that of a double clarinet than of a conical oboe, since it is the bore, rather than type of reed, which determines the tone. It is lower, and as it is not shrill, it is often combined with other instruments and used to accompany a singer.

Most bagpipes of the western world also belong to the class of double-reeds. Most of the drones (except the Italian *zampogna*) have single reeds, but the chanter, or melody pipe, has a double reed and a conical bore, so may be called an 'oboe' type. The Scottish pipes, like all others, originated in the Islamic world, crossed, as so many other instruments—lutes, drums, shawms, horn-pipes, etc.—into Spain, and eventually reached Scotland, where its spread and development were rapid. Today, if you ask an Arab in Jordan, for example, if anyone plays the bagpipes, he will probably return not with the indigenous variety, but with a local musician carrying a fine set of Scottish Highland pipes!

Reed for a *ghaita* (shawm).

Broad reed, with regulators, for a cylindrical oboe.

Double Reed Instruments—Shawms (Oboes)

M1   *Zurna*. Conical shawm. Baghdad, Iraq.
L: 36·5 cm

M2   *Ghaita*. Conical shawm in case. Fez, Morocco.
L: 38·5 cm

M3   *Saz*. Conical shawm. Qashqai nomads near
Shiraz, Iran. L: 33·5 cm

M4   *Shahnāy*. Conical shawm. Jodhpur, India.
L: 33 cm

M5   *Surnai*. Conical shawm in case. Uzbek people,
North Afghanistan. L: 49·5 cm

M6   *Karna*. Trumpet bell, to which the reed mechanism of a shawm has been added to make for easier playing. Qashqai nomads near Shiraz, Iran.
L: 70·5 cm

M7   *Shahnāy*. Conical shawm. Lucknow, India.
L: 39 cm

M8   *Sarune*. Small conical shawm. Karo Batak people,
Sumatra, Indonesia. L: 24 cm

M9   *Surnai*. Conical shawm. Kota Baharu, Malaysia.
L: 43 cm

M10   *Sona*. Conical shawm. Peking, China. L: 28 cm

M11   *Balaban*. Cylindrical oboe with broad reed. Tabriz,
Iran. L: 40 cm

M12   *Mey*. Cylindrical oboe with broad reed.
Ankara, Turkey. L: 45·5 cm

M13   *Kwan*. Cylindrical oboe with broad reed. Peking,
China. L: 27 cm

M14   *Kwan*. Double cylindrical oboe with broad reeds.
Peking, China. L: 21·5 cm

Ghaita **M2** players using continuous breathing; their cheeks serve as a wind reservoir. Marrakesh, Morocco.

Ghaita **M2** player gathering the wedding guests. Tlemcen, Algeria.

The *karna* **M6** of the Qashqai nomads. Near Shiraz, Iran.

The *balaban* **M11** has a very broad double reed with a
regulator set into a cylindrical pipe. Kurdistan, Iran.

Drums and Rhythms

Rhythm is an essential part of all music, and in many regions of the Islamic world it attains a high level of subtlety and sophistication. Rhythm is inherent in any melody, but we shall concentrate in this section on rhythms produced on instruments which are designed to produce rhythm: i.e., drums and other percussion instruments.

A rhythmic accompaniment will always be cyclic and based on a metre—the same rhythmic structure being repeated continuously, although with variation. In the Arab world the basic metres have been noted down by famous theorists and are considered to belong to the *iqa'at* system of rhythmic modes. The late French baron Rodolphe d'Erlanger in *La Musique Arabe*, Vol. VI, has noted down not less than 111 basic metres with their appropriate names without taking the rhythms of North Africa into account. Some of these metres are very short, others are very long: there are metres of 2 beats and others of up to 88 beats. Each of them is defined by the durational relationship of the accents, but not only by that. The Arabs distinguish basically between two sonorities on a rhythmic instrument: the light *tak* and the dark *dum*. Between the *tak* and the *dum* they reckon with five secondary sonorities. The sonority of each single fundamental beat is important for the definition of the metre.

What is true of Arab rhythms is true of Turkish and Persian rhythms as well. A particular kind of rhythm, often called *aksak* in Turkish is met with not only in the art music, but also in the folk music of western and European Turkey, the Balkans and the Gulf area. *Aksak* is a Turkish 9-rhythm: $2+2+2+3$, but has recently been more and more accepted as a general term for rhythmic patterns combining units of 2 and 3. Some examples of common Bahraini rhythms may be used for illustration: the two rhythms connected with dance-songs called *saut* are: an 8-rhythm $3+2+2+1$

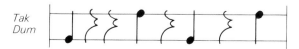

and a 6-rhythm: $2 + 1\frac{1}{2} + 1\frac{1}{2} + 1$

And one of the traditional rhythms known for the accompaniment to *jirba* **L5** or bagpipe music is this 20 rhythm: $3 + 4 + 3 + 3 + 2 + 2 + 3$

The drums used for the *saut* are four *muruas* **P2**, if the song is produced by a soloist playing an *'ud* **A1**; in other cases the drums will be a *tabl* and a number of *ṭar*. The *jirba* music requires a number (in general four or five) of cylindrical drums called *tabl*.

Many Middle Eastern song genres may be defined with reference to their poetic form. But as soon as they are dance songs and thus dependent on a regular metre, they may as easily be defined in respect of the rhythmic pattern of the percussion accompaniment. To some extent it is true that the instruments needed for the percussion accompaniment may depend on the song genre. If the Bahraini *saut* needs four *muruas*, the Bahraini *bastah* would need a *darabuka* **O7–11** and a *def* **P10**. But both genres could be presented with *tabl* and *ṭar*.

The drums of the Middle East are, roughly speaking, of four kinds. 1) The goblet drum is highly regarded. It is called *zarb* or *dombak* in Iran **O6**, *darabuka* or *tabl* in the Arab world, *darabuka* or *deblek* in Turkey. It is used both in classical and folk music. 2) The frame drum with inserted cymbals may be called *duff* or *def*. In some parts of the Arab world a small instrument of the kind is named *reqq*, a large one *bendir*. A one-skin frame drum without cymbals, but usually with iron rings or small bells inside the frame would in the Gulf area invariably be considered a *ṭar*, but may in other parts of the Middle East be looked upon as a *duff* or a *daira*. In the Arabian desert and in the Sahara the nomads may use a circular frame drum with two skins. In the Maghreb a square drum with two skins is in use **P9**. A *duff* (with cymbals) may take part in the Sufi or dervish music and in classical music, and the *ṭar* may be heard in connection with different kinds of religious music (as the *mauled*), but these two instruments as well as the others mentioned above belong primarily to folk music. 3) The two-skin drums which are not frame drums, but barrel shaped or cylindrical drums are folk instruments and prominent in this sphere just as they were in the Turkish military bands (*mehterhane*). Among the names for the big drums are *davul* (Turkey), *tabl* (Arab regions) **P1** and *dahal* (Persia). 4) The kettledrums belong to military music and religious (Sufi) music, and to classical music too. All over the Middle East one of the most common names for kettledrums is *nakkare* or *naqqāra* **O1** and **4** Other names are *kudum* **O3** and *mousaher* **O2**, the latter being held in the hands of the musician. In short, every region seems to have produced a local variant either in name, in usage, or in the instrument itself.

Rhythm may be played on instruments other than drums. One important one is the hands of the human beings. Hand-clapping—alone or together with drumming—is, in the whole of the Middle East, a most popular kind of rhythmic accompaniment and so is (although to a lesser degree) the sound produced by two fingers rubbed quickly against each other. Furthermore there are cymbals, called *zil* in Turkey, *sangat* or *tusut* in Arab countries, spoons **N2** and **3** and other clappers, jew's harps **N15–19** and many other instruments.

What has been said about the rhythms of the Middle East and North Africa is equally true for the rest of the Islamic world. The rhythms of Islamic Africa south of the Sahara or of Pakistan and North India may be amazing in their refinement. Who would not feel the enchantment of the classical Indian drumming on a pair of *tabla* **D1** or on a *pakhawaj*? The basis of it is given with the rhythmic patterns called *talas* and as in the Middle East the sonority of the beat takes part in the definition of a particular *tala*. Each combination of strokes (with fingers, palm, and use of both hands) and the placing of the stroke (near the rim of the drum head, in the centre or in between) has a name, a *bol*, and a particular *tala* is ultimately defined by the suite of the *bols* belonging to its basic pattern.

Thus the 12-rhythm *ektala*, commonly used in the single style called *khyal* can be presented like this:

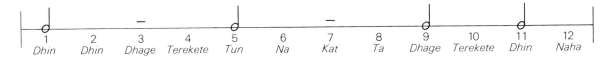

1	2	3	4	5	6	7	8	9	10	11	12
Dhin	*Dhin*	*Dhage*	*Terekete*	*Tun*	*Na*	*Kat*	*Ta*	*Dhage*	*Terekete*	*Dhin*	*Naha*

In the Middle East as well as in Islamic Africa and Afghanistan, rhythm solos may be performed publicly and then most often on a goblet drum. In Pakistan and North India such rhythm solos have recently become quite common even at classical concerts; and they are consequently most of the time heard on *tabla*. In short, in the Islamic world we encounter rhythms far more complex and varied than those in use in Europe.

Drums and Rhythm

N1 *Mihbash*. Coffee pounder (pestle and mortar). Damascus, Syria. (A definite rhythm is used in order to gather the neighbours.) L: pestle 61 cm; mortar 32 cm

N2 *Kaşik*. Pair of wooden spoons. Istanbul, Turkey. L: 19 cm

N3 *Kaşik*. Pair of wooden spoons. Crete, Greece. L: 20 cm

N4 *Çalpara*. Pair of wooden clappers. Istanbul, Turkey. L: 19 cm

N5 *Qaraqeb*. Pair of iron cymbals. Marrakesh, Morocco. L: 29 cm

N6 *Qaraqeb*. Two pairs of iron clappers. Marrakesh, Morocco. L: 30 cm

N7 *Jhanj*. Pair of brass cymbals. Lucknow, India. L: 10 cm

N8 *Kartal*. Two pairs of wooden clappers with jingles. Lucknow, India. L: 24 cm

N9 *Chimta*. Jingling tongs. Jaipur, India. L: 87 cm

N10 *Qaraqeb*. Pair of iron clappers. Agadez, Niger. L: 24 cm

N11 *Zilli maşa*. Jingling tongs. Istanbul, Turkey. L: 37·5 cm

N12   *Manjur*. Rattling hoofs on a canvas apron. Manama, Bahrain. L: 73 cm

N13   *Shantou*. Gourd stomper. Beri Beri people, Niger. L: 61 cm

N14   *Dombo*. Gourd with two beaters. Dosso, Niger. L: 49 cm

N15   *Chang*. Seven iron jew's harps with steel tongues. Baluchistan, Pakistan. L: from 12·5 to 19 cm

N16   *Chank*. Four iron jew's harps with steel tongues. Kabul, Afghanistan. L: from 9 to 11 cm

N17   *Bambaro*. Two iron jew's harps with steel tongues. Zinder, Niger. L: 6 cm

N18   *Scacciapensieri*. Iron jew's harp with steel tongue. Sicily, Italy. L: 10 cm

N19   *Gengong*. Bamboo jew's harp. Sumatra, Indonesia. L: 16 cm

N20   Orchestra: brass statuettes of seven musicians, made by the *cire perdue* method. They are playing assorted instruments: *shantou, godjie, tabl, kakaki* and *saréoua*. Niamey, Niger. L: c. 15–20 cm each

N21   Statuette of double drummer made of bronze by the *cire perdue* method and used as a gold weight. Ashanti region, Ghana. L: 7 cm

Drums : Kettledrums and Goblet drums

O1   *Tbilat*. Pair of earthenware drums. Marrakesh, Morocco. L: 44 cm

O2   *Mousaher*. Pair of small brass kettledrums. Played with drums in the hands. Used by dervish orders especially during the Ramadan. Damascus, Syria. L: 15 cm

O3   *Kudum*. Pair of copper kettledrums with beaters. Istanbul, Turkey. L: 23·5 cm

O4   *Naqqāra*. Kettledrum with iron body. Omdurman, Sudan. L: 53 cm

O5   *Douma*. Two gourd kettledrums with snares. Dosso, Niger. L: 35·5 cm

O6   *Zarb*. Wooden goblet drum. Teheran, Iran. L: 45·5 cm

O7 *Darabuka*. Pottery goblet drum. Algiers, Algeria. L: 41 cm

O8 *Darabuka*. Wooden goblet drum. Marsh Arabs, Iraq. L: 35 cm

O9 *Harrazi*. Earthenware goblet drum. Hamatchas' brotherhood drum. Fez, Morocco. L: 44·5 cm

O10 *Agoual*. Footed earthenware goblet drum. Fez, Morocco. L: 49·5 cm

O11 *Darabuka*. Brass goblet drum. Fez, Morocco. L: 39 cm

O12 *Tarijas*. Various sizes of small pottery goblet drums. Fez and Meknes, Morocco. L: 11·5 cm– 26 cm

Drums : Tabls and Tambourines

P1 *Tabl*. Cylindrical, double-headed drum. Beni Malal, Morocco. L: 36 cm

P2 *Muruas*. Little cylindrical, double-headed drum. Manama, Bahrain. L: 16 cm

P3 *Ganga*. Wooden, double-headed frame-drum. Sahara, Algeria. L: 45 cm

P4 *Bendir*. Large frame-drum with a snare. Ouzad, Morocco. L: 37·5 cm

P5 *Daira*. Frame drum. Samarkand, Uzbekistan, USSR. L: 42 cm

P6 *Duff*. Large frame-drum. Damascus, Syria. L: 56·4 cm

P7 *Daira*. Frame drum. Tashqurghan, Afghanistan. L: 43 cm

P8 *Daira*. Pellet drum. Double-headed circular frame drum on a wooden stick; a children's toy. Tashqurghan, Afghanistan. L: 30·5 cm

P9 *Duff*. Square frame-drum, covered with skin. Ghardaia, Algeria. L: 23·2 cm

P10 *Def*. Three frame drums with cymbals inserted. Damascus, Syria. L: 21·5 cm

P11 *Daira*. Frame drum, inlaid with *khatam* work. Teheran, Iran. L: 36·5 cm

Dindoun is rhythmic music used at feasts and celebrations, especially at weddings, provided by people who came originally from Black Africa, on the iron cymbals called *qaraqeb* **N5**. Marrakesh, Morocco.

Kaşik or *kashik* **N2** and **3** are wooden spoons used as rhythmic accompaniment to folk songs, but occasionally for solos by virtuosi in eastern Greece and Turkey. Crete, Greece. (G.B.)

The *chang* **N15** or jew's harp is usually used as a quiet solo instrument for love songs but recently it is replacing the drum as a rhythm instrument in groups of 3 or 4 musicians. Jodhpur, India.

Even a couple of pairs of small tea cups can form an instrument for rhythmic accompaniment to song. Amman, Jordan.

Beating on a wheel drum gives a sharp rhythmical emphasis to other drums and clappers. Marrakesh, Morocco.

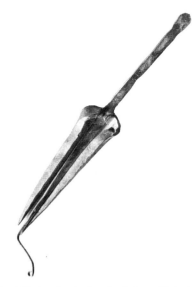

Chang **N15** or iron jew's harp. Quetta, Pakistan. (G.B.)

Chank **N16**, a slender iron jew's harp. Kabul, Afghanistan. (G.B.)

Scacciapensieri. A large iron jew's harp, with an almost circular frame. Sicily, Italy. (G.B.)

A gold weight, made of bronze by the *cire perdue* method, which shows a drummer beating on two kettledrums. Ashanti, Ghana. (G.B.)

Three types of goblet drums: *darabuka* **O7** (left) from Tunis, but acquired in Algiers; *zarb* **O6** (centre), a fine 18th-century solo instrument intricately inlaid with *khatam* work, Teheran, Iran; *darabuka* (right) inlaid with wood and plastic, Damascus, Syria. (G.B.)

A member of one of the brotherhoods using the *darabuka* in religious music. Fez, Morocco.

The *tabl* is part of the *gnaoua* groups which play in the great square. Marrakesh, Morocco.

The large cylindrical drum, *tabl* such as **P1**, is used with the double *naqqāra* and the *ghaita* (shawm) to head a wedding procession. Tlemcen, Algeria.

The *daira* is used by dervish orders to help attain ecstasy. Sanandaj, Iran.

A *duff* used in classical music. Peshawar, Pakistan.

The double *naqqāra* is beaten with two sticks by the nomadic Beni Amer people who live on the borders of Sudan and Eritrea. Near Agordat, Ethiopia.

A religious dance on Friday mornings is accompanied by *duff* (frame drum) and *naqqāra* (kettledrum). Beni Amer people near Agordat, Ethiopia.

A selection of drums : double *naqqāra* from Rabat, Morocco ; square *duff* **P9** from Fez, Morocco ; three *defs* or tambourines from Damascus, Syria ; a large *daira* with rings to jingle, inlaid all over the front with *khatam* work, Teheran, Iran ; an *agoual*, tall goblet drum from Fez, Morocco ; and six examples of the *tarijas* used by children in Fez, Morocco. (G.B.)

Plate 1. Playing the *satara* **K7** (two duct flutes) to accompany singing in Baluchistan. Quetta, Pakistan.

Plate 2. Girls celebrating the birthday of the Prophet, singing to the accompaniment of the *bendir* **P4**. Ouzad, Morocco.

Plate 3. An old man in the western desert of Rajasthan playing the *kemayche* **I9** while singing a ballad. West of Jaeselmer, India.

Plate 4. Bedouin man playing the *rebab* **H2**. Abu Dhabi. (P.R.O.)

Plate 5. The *sarangi* **I5** used as a solo instrument in classical music. Lahore, Pakistan.

Plate 6. The *nay* **K2** is used for classical music, and also accompanies the Mevlevi dervishes of Konya. Istanbul, Turkey.

Plate 7. The *murli* **L13** is a single reed instrument with a drone. Although this man is a snake charmer he plays all the folk music of the region. Borunda, Rajasthan, India.

Plate 8. Playing the hornpipe *zamr* **L8**. Foum el Ançun, Morocco.

Plate 9. To play the *ghaita* **M2** with non-stop breathing the player's cheeks act as a wind reservoir. Marrakesh, Morocco.

Plate 10. The ‘*ud* **A1** maker playing his own lute. Algiers, Algeria.

Plate 11. The *chang* **N15** or jew's harp replaces the drum in this group of Baluchi musicians, singing to the accompaniment of *dhambura* **E1** (centre) and *saroz* **I11**. Quetta, Pakistan.

Plate 12. The fiddle of this 13th century Spanish manuscript shows the influence of Islamic fiddles such as the *kemençe* **I1** on European music of that time.
© British Museum.

Islamic Influences on the Music of the World

The musical culture area of the Islamic world stretches for thousands of miles, and Moroccans travelling to Turkestan would feel at home with the music despite all local differences (particularly in instruments). In the sphere of classical music the types of modal scales, of vocal ornamentation, of intricate rhythms and of melody instruments are familiar in all Muslim areas. There is a great deal more variation in folk music, but here too there are fundamental similarities. Just as the call to Prayer can be heard from Timbuktu to Djakarta, so we also find wedding guests summoned by the *surnai* and *naqqāra* and *tabl* in the whole of that vast region, and wherever there are nomads we find poetry sung to the accompaniment of the simple one-string *rabāb*,

But the music of the Islamic peoples has also had considerable influence on the music of other peoples. In the Far East, for example, a number of instruments have been incorporated into Chinese music. The short lute, which was found in Central Asia about two thousand years ago, was taken further east by the sixth century; in China it is called the *p'i p'a*; from there it reached Japan and Korea. Along the same route travelled cymbals, certain long trumpets, the conical shawm (*sona*) **Q2** and cylindrical oboe **Q3** and all the fiddles, such as the *er-hu* as well as the long lutes, called the *san hsien* **Q4** in China, *shamisen* in Japan and *shanz* in Mongolia. Much later the Persian *santur* or dulcimer **B2** was adopted by the Chinese as the 'foreign zither' (as opposed to the long zithers of the Far East) and this *yang ch'in* **Q1** is a popular instrument just as it was in most of Europe in the Middle Ages and until the eighteenth century.

If the Far East, India and South-east Asia owe a debt to the music of the Islamic world, we in Europe owe an

The *sona* **Q2** and **M10** or conical shawm. Peking, China. (G.B.)

85

Kwan **M14** or cylindrical oboe, resembling in size and shape the Arabic double clarinets. Peking, China. (G.B.)

even larger one, in musical styles as well as instruments. Indeed, most European instruments had their ancestry in North Africa and the Middle East. They reached Europe by different routes, but it seems evident that three historical events were of primary importance. The Arab conquest of Spain in 710–13 is the first of these. During the whole of the Middle Ages, Spain (Al-Andalus) was one of the spiritual hearts of Europe; for several centuries musical ideas and theories spread over the continent from Córdoba, Toledo, Malaga, Seville and Granada. The Christians discovered the *'ud* and made their lute in its image. It is likely that the *rebec* was taken over from the Andalusian *rabāb*, but it may just as well have entered Europe via the Crusade, the second historical event of importance. Out of different fiddles of Arabic origin our violin evolved. One of the effects of the Crusades was the establishment of new contacts between western Europe and the Levant. The Christian warriors were impressed by the Muslim kettledrums, *naqqāra*, and introduced them in their homelands. The straight-sided *tabl*, the frame drum with cymbals which we call tambourine **P10** as well as cymbals and the trumpets called *nafir* **K12**, the shrill conical shawm—all these military instruments came to Europe with the returning Crusaders.

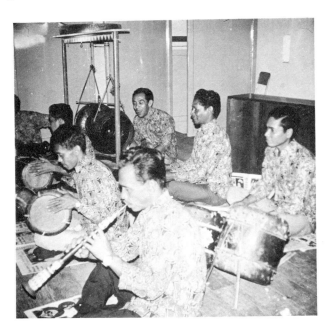

A Malay puppet show with its orchestra led by a *surnai* **M9** or shawm. Kota Baharu, Malaysia.

The decorated *surnai* **M9** of the shadow play orchestra. Kota Baharu, Malaysia. (G.B.)

In the sixteenth century the third of these historical events took place when the Turks became the masters of the Balkans. They took with them a musical style, including the modal system of the *makams* and a series of complicated rhythms, which are still in use in countries like Greece, Bulgaria, Albania, Yugoslavia. And Turkish instruments such as the oboe, *zurna*, with its inseparable companion, the great two-skin drum *davul*, are still popular instruments at festive occasions (especially at weddings) in the whole of the Balkans. So too are the bagpipes which we owe to Islamic countries, and the *cymbalom* (dulcimer) of Hungary, the *kaval* **K3** or end-blown flute of Bulgaria, the *chifte* or double clarinet of Albania. The zithers sparked off a great development which culminated in harpsichords and other keyboards.

We cannot know how great the influences from Andalusian and Middle Eastern sources on European art music have been. But evidence such as the thirteenth century Spanish manuscript in the British Museum giving the names of the modes for each song suggests that it may have been considerable. Certainly the folk music of the northern coast of the Mediterranean Sea still bears traces of the Islamic singing and instrumental styles. In addition, our mediaeval military music owes not only the actual instruments but also many of the social restrictions and privileges of the Middle Eastern musicians to Islamic countries. The right to own trumpets and kettledrums was restricted to the nobility in Europe as it was farther east. Futhermore the low social status of professional musicians reflects the anti-music attitude of the early legalists of Islam.

Picturesque acknowledgments of the existence of at least certain kinds of Turkish and Arabian music are met with at a very much later date in western art music. Mozart's *Alla Turca Rondo* in the Piano Sonata in A major as well as several sections from his *Entführung*, and Beethoven's Turkish March from *The Ruins of Athens* are examples of this kind of influence. In recent years avant-garde music and rock music show other developments along similar lines.

In the last century, however, considerable development in the opposite direction has led to the establishment of

European conservatories of music in most capitals of the Middle East and to the forming of symphony orchestras and western inspired ensembles of musicians. And if eastern folk fiddles inspired the western violin, this same violin is now back in the east, replacing the *kamān* or *kamāncha* in classical music. Sometimes, as is the case in Pakistan and North India, it creates a place of its own, side by side with the traditional fiddles. The harmonium **Q8**, introduced by missionaries, has also been transformed into a drone instrument all over the Indian sub-continent.

The classical western music of the nineteenth century and the commercial music of more recent years has lately been imitated by the local composers and pop musicians of the east. The introduction of tape recorders, transistor radios, and TV sets has hastened the spread of pop music and has often replaced local music, which is no longer learned by oral tradition from a folk or classical musician of the area. Mechanical means of music learning have short circuited traditional methods and the result has been that it is often true today that only a few old singers and instrumentalists know the best music of an area. Microphones—now such a status symbol that many musicians will not perform without them—have changed both vocal and instrumental technique so that quality performances have tended to decline.

Modern communications, however, have resulted in two factors recently which may reverse this trend: international music congresses have stressed the necessity to encourage the best music in each country, and gramophone records of the finest musicians in the Islamic world are becoming available to all people in those lands. One can only hope that this interaction of east and west in music will be as fruitful as it has been throughout the centuries.

The tiny *sarune* **M8** of the Batak people leads an orchestra of gongs. Near Lake Toba, Sumatra, Indonesia. (G.B.)

Some Instruments of East and West

Q1   *Yang ch'in*. Dulcimer. Peking, China. L: 76 cm

Q2   *Sona*. Conical shawm. Peking, China. L: 28 cm

Q3   *Kwan*. Cylindrical oboe. Peking, China. L: 21·5 cm

Q4   *San hsien*. Long lute. Peking, China. L: 93 cm

Q5   *Gayda*. Bagpipes. Sofia, Bulgaria. L: 76 cm

Q6   Violin. London, England. L: 59 cm

Q7   S-shaped trumpet, to show the twelfth century shape. Maker: Philip Bate, London, 1975. L: 98 cm

Q8   Harmonium. Lucknow, India. L: 54·5 cm

Q9   Engraving of Philippe Galle (1537–1612), Haarlem, Netherlands, showing European instruments of the sixteenth century including: lutes, viols, harps, trumpets, shawms, panpipes, tambourines, triangle and kettledrums. L: 28·5 cm

Q10   Engraving from a Dutch encyclopaedia of the eighteenth century illustrating 'The Musical Instruments of the Bible' from those in contemporary use in Holland. Most of these show considerable influence from the Islamic world of music. L: 39·5 cm

Bibliography

In this bibliography we have tried to include writings from the Islamic world itself as well as those available in European languages but the shortage of time has prevented a more complete and better researched compilation.

Abbasuddin Ahmed *Folksongs of East Pakistan* (July, 1956).

Abdu-l-Wahab 'Le développement de la musique arabe en Orient, Espagne et Tunisie', *Revue Tunisienne*, xxv (1918), 106–17.

Ackerman, P. 'The Character of Persian Music', *A Survey of Persian Art from Prehistoric Times to the Present*, ed. P. Ackerman and A. U. Pope, iii (Oxford, 1939) 2805–18.

Advielle, V. *La musique chez les Persans en 1885* (includes: 'Instruments de 18 empire persan . . . de . . . Ali Ekber Khan') (Paris, 1885).

Agrawala, V. S. 'Some Early References to Musical Ragas and Instruments', *Journal of the Music Academy, Madras*, xxiii (1952), 113.

Aguilar y Tejera, A. 'De música marroqui', *Revista de la raza* (1928).

Ahmed, A. M. 'The Lahjat-i-Sikandar Shahi, a Unique Book on Indian Music of the Time of Sikandar Lodi (1489–1517)', *Islamic Culture*, xxviii (1954), 410–17.

Ahmed, A. M. 'Bei uns in Arabien', *Kontakt* (1958), 140.

Ahmed, A. M. 'Muslim Attitude and Contribution to Music in India', *Zeitschrift der Deutschen Morgenländischen Gesellschaft*, cxix (1969), 86–92.

Ahrens, C. *Instrumentale Musikstile an der osttürkischen Schwarzmeerküste: eine vergleichende Untersuchung der Spielpraxis von Davul-Zurna, Kemençe und Tulum* (Munich, 1970).

Aima, M. L. 'Musical Instruments', *Kashmir* (May and June, 1959).

Aissou, Si Kâmil Hussein 'Musique et mystique au Maroc', in **Porte** i (1968) 464–8.

Akbarov, I. A., ed. *Uzbekskaya narodnaya muzyka* (Uzbek folk music) (Tashkent, 1952).

Alexandru, T. *Muzica populara banateana* (Folk music of the Banat) (Bucharest, 1942).

Alexandru, T. *Instrumentele muzicale ale poporului Romîn* (The Musical Instruments of the Rumanian people) (Bucharest, 1956).

Alexandru, T. 'Tilinca, ein uraltes rumänisches Volksinstrument', *Studie Memoriae Belae Bartók Sacra* (Budapest, 1956, 3/1959), 107–21.

Alexandru, T. 'The Study of Folk Musical Instruments in the Rumanian People's Republic', *Journal of the International Folk Music Council*, xii (1960), 13–16.

Alexandru, T. 'Les instruments musicaux du folklore égyptien et ceux du pays des Balkans', *Rad XV-og kongresa savenza udruženja folklorista jugoslavije u Jajai 12–16 Septembra 1968* (Sarajevo, 1971), 327–40.

Allahwerdy, M. *Philosophie de la musique orientale* (Damascus, 1948).

Allende, U. *All-India Music Conference, Report of the Second* (Delhi, 1919).

Anderson, L. A. 'The Interrelation of African and Arab Musics: Some Preliminary Considerations', *Essays on Music and History in Africa*, ed. K. P. Klaus (Evanston, 1971), 143–69.

Ankermann, B. 'Die afrikanischen Musikinstrumente', *Ethnologisches Notizblatt*, iii (1901), 1–185.

Antoni, L. *Folklori muzikor shqiptar* (Albanian folk music) (Pristen, 1972).

Arasli, A. 'Dis Türk musikileri: Tatar musikisi' (Turkic musics: Tatar musics), *Musiki mecmuasi*, no. 270 (1972), 18–19.

Arel, H. S. *Türk musikisi kimindir?* (To whom does Turkish music belong?) (Istanbul, 1939–40/R1969).

Arseven, V. 'Artvin-Y sufeli türkülerinden birkaç örnek' (A few examples of *türküler* from Artvin-Yusuf), *Türk folklor arastirmalari*, no. 243 (1969), 5429–31.

Arseven, V. 'Halk Türkülerimizin yayginligu' (Diffusion of Turkish folksongs), *Türk folklor araştirmalari*, no. 266 (1971), 6077–8.

Arslanoglu, C. 'Posofta giyim, calgi, oyun ve düğün geleneği' (Traditions of dress, music, dance and wedding in Posof), *Türk folklor araştirmalari*, no. 215 (1967), 4139–40.

Arsunar, F. 'Kisázsiai török pentaton dallamok (Des mélodies pentatones des Turcs d'Asie Mineure)', *Mélanges offerts à Zoltan Kodály à l'occasion de son 60ième anniversaire* (Budapest, 1943), 322–8.

Askew, G. *A Bibliography of the Bagpipe* (Newcastle upon Tyne, 1932).

Aubry, P. 'Au Turkestan; notes sur quelques habitudes musicales, *Mercure musicale*, i (1905), 97–108.

Audisio, G. 'Les soirées de Baghdad', *Revue musicale*, xi/102 (March 1930), 219–28.

Avenary, H. 'Abu'l-Salt's Treatise on Music', *Musica disciplina*, vi (1952), 27–32.

Avenary, H. 'Magic, Symbolism and Allegory of the Old-Hebrew Sound-Instruments', *Collectanea historiae musicae*, ii (1956), 21–32.

Azer, E. and Mounir, F. 'Folklore world: records of foik (sic) music and songs' *al-Funūn al-Shaābia*, vi (1968), 104–12 (in Arabic with English summary).

Azzawi, A. *Iraqian Music under the Mongols and the Turkmans 1258–1534* (Baghdad, 1951).

Bachmann, W. *Die Anfange des Streichinstrumentenspiels* (Leipzig, 1964, 2/1966; Eng. trans. 1969).

Baines, A. *Woodwind Instruments and their History* (London, 1957, 2/1962).

Baines, A. *Bagpipes* (Oxford, 1960).

Bake, A. 'The Music of India', *New Oxford History of Music*, i *Ancient and Oriental Music* (London, 1957), 195–227.

Balanchivadze, V., Donadze, V. and Tsutsua, P. *Grousinskaia muzikalnaia kultura* (The musical culture of the Georgians) (Moscow, 1957).

Balfour, H. 'The Old British "Pibcorn" or "Hornpipe" and its Affinities', *Journal of the Anthropological Institute of Great Britain*, xx (1891), 142–54.

Balfour, H. *Musical Instruments from the Siamese Malay States and Perak* (Liverpool, 1904).

Baljon, J. M. S. *Moslimse ambivalentie inzake muziek* (Moslem ambivalence concerning music) (Leiden, 1968).

Ballero, M. 'Musique et société dans l'Inde du nord', *La musique dans la vie*, ii (1969), 71–95.

Baloch, N. A. *Musical Instruments of the Lower Indus Valley of Sind* (Hyderabad, 1966).

Barbès, L. L. 'La musique musulmane en Algérie', *Information coloniale*, no. 33 (1947).

Barblan, G. *Musiche e strumenti musicali dell'Africa orientale italiana* (Naples, 1941).

Barkechli, M. *L'art Sassanide, base de la musique arabe* (Teheran, 1947).

Barkechli, M. 'La gamme de la musique iranienne', *Annales des Télécommunications*, v (May, 1950), 5.

Barkechli, M. 'La gamme persane et ses rapports avec la gamme occidentale', *Olympia*, i (1950), 53.

Barkechli, M. 'La musique iranienne', *L'histoire de la musique*, i ed. Roland-Manuel, *Encyclopédie de la Pléiade*, ix (Paris, 1960), 453–525.

Barkechli, M. and Marouffi, M. *La musique traditionnelle de l'Iran* (1963).

Barnett, R. D. 'New Facts about Musical Instruments from Ur', *Iraq*, xxxi (London, 1969), 96–103.

Bartók, B. *Cântece popolare românesti din Cimitatul Bihor* (Bucharest, 1913).

Bartók, B. 'Die Volksmusik der Araber von Biskra und Umgebung', *Zeitschrift für Musikwissenschaft*, ii (1919–20), 489–522.

Bartók, B. 'Auf Volkslied-Forschungsfahrt in der Türkei', *Musik der Zeit*, iii (1953), 23–6.

Basden, G. T. *Niger Ibos* (London, 1938) (Chapter xvii—*Music*).

Basgöz, I. 'Turkish Hikaye—telling Tradition in Azerbaijan, Iran', *Journal of American Folklore*, lxxxiii (1970), 391–405.

Basset, R. *L'insurrection algérienne de 1871 dans les chansons populaires Kabyles* (Louvain, 1892).

Battesti, T. 'La musique traditionnelle iranienne: aspects socio-historiques', *Objets et mondes*, ix (1969), 317–40.

Baud-Bovy, S. 'L'accord de la Lyre antique et la musique populaire de la Grèce moderne', *Revue de musicologie*, liii (1967), 1–20.

Bebey, F. *Musique de l'Afrique* (Paris, 1969; revised Eng. trans., 1975).

Behn, F. 'Die Laute im Altertum und frühen Mittelalter', *Zeitschrift für Musikwissenschaft*, i (1918–19), 89–107.

Beichert, E. A. *Die Wissenschaft der Musik bei Al Farabi* (diss., Berlin Univ., 1936).

Belayev, V. 'Khoresmian Notation', *The Sackbut*, iv (1923–4), 171–3.

Belayev, V. 'Turkomanian Music', *Pro Musica Quarterly*, v/1 (1927), 4; v/2 (1927), 9.

Belayev, V. 'The Folk-music of Georgia', *Musical Quarterly*, xix (1933), 417–33.

Belayev, V. 'The Longitudinal Open Flutes of Central Asia', *Musical Quarterly*, xix (1933), 84–100.

Belayev, V. *Muzykalnye instrumenty uzbekistana* (Musical instruments of Uzbekistan) (Moscow, 1933).

Belayev, V. 'Turkish Music', *Musical Quarterly*, xxi (1935), 356–67.

Belayev, V. 'A népi harmóniarendszer' (The harmonic system of the folk), *Emlékkönyv Kodály Zoltán 70. születésnapjára* (Budapest, 1953), 75–86.

Belayev, V. *Ocherki po istorii muzyki narodov SSSR* (Notes on the history of music of the peoples of the USSR) (Moscow, 1962–3).

Bentzon, A. F. W. *The Launeddas: a Sardinian Folk Music Instrument* (Copenhagen, 1969).

Bernard, R. 'Congrès de musique marocaine à Fès', *Revue musicale* xx/194 (1939), 164–9.

Berner, A. *Studien zur arabischen Musik auf der Grund der gegenwartigen Theorie und Praxis in Egypten* (diss., Berlin Univ. 1935; Leipzig, 1937).

Berner, A. 'Neue Bestrebungen der arabischen Musik in Aegypten', *Allgemeine musikalische Zeitung* (1942).

Bertholon, L. and Chantre, E. *Recherches anthropologiques dans la Berberie Orientale : Tripolitaine, Tunisie, Algérie* (Lyons, 1913) (Chapter 6: 'La Musique et la Danse').

Besner, F. E. 'An Hausa Song from Katsina', *Ethnomusicology*, xiv (1970), 418–38.

Besner, F. E. *Kidàn dárán sàllà : Music for the Eve of the Muslim Festivals of ''Id al-Fitr' and ''Id al-Kabir' in Kano* (Bloomington, 1974).

Bhanu, D. 'The Promotion of Music by the Turko-Afghan Rulers of India', *Islamic Culture*, xxix (1955), 9–31.

Bhatkande, N. V. *A Short Historical Survey of the Music of Upper India* (Bombay, 1934).

Blades, J. *Percussion Instruments and their History* (London, 1970).

Blom, E., ed. *Grove's Dictionary of Music and Musicians* (London, rev. 5/1954).

Blume, F., ed. *Die Musik in Geschichte und Gegenwart* (Kassel, 1958–).

Bogdanova, L. 'Pesni i predaniia za pomokhamedanchvaneto vûv folklora na podopskite bûlgari' (Songs and legends of Islamization in the folklore of Bulgarian Rhodope), *Narodnostna i bitova obshtnost na rodopskite bulgari*, ed. Ts. Romanska (Sofia, 1969), 221–40 (Russian and French summaries).

Borrel, E. 'La musique turque', *Revue de musicologie*, vi (1922), 149–61; vii (1923), 26–32, 60–70.

Borrel, E. 'Contribution à la bibliographie de la musique turque au XX siècle', *Revue des études islamiques*, ii (1928), 513.

Borrel, E. 'Publications musicologiques turques', *Revue de musicologie*, xiv (1933), 235–6.

Borrel, E. 'Le crise de la musique en Oriente', *Guide musical* (Paris, 1934).

Borrel, E. 'Sur la musique secrète des tribus turques Alévi', *Revue des études islamiques*, vii (1934), 241–50.

Borrel, E. 'La musique turque', *La musique des origines à nos jours*, ed. N. Dufourcq (Paris, 1946), 433–7.

Borrel, E. 'Les poetes Kizil Bach et leur musique', *Revue des études islamiques*, xv (1947), 157–90.

Borsai, I. 'Mélodie traditionnelles des Égyptiens et leur importance dans la recherche de l'ancienne musique pharaonique', *Studia musicologica*, x (Budapest, 1968), 69–90.

Boubakeur, Si Hamza 'Psalmodie coranique', in **Porte** i (1968), 388–403.

Boucheman, A. de 'Quartorze chansons de l'Arabie du Nord accompagnées à la rabába', *Bulletin d'études orientales*, xi (1945–6), 31–46.

Bowles, E. A. 'Eastern Influences on the Use of Trumpets and Drums during the Middle Ages', *Anuario musical*, xxvi (1971), 1–28.

Boyce, M. *The Manichean Hymn Cycles in Parthian* (Oxford, 1954) (For iconographic sources of the history of Persian music).

Buhle, E. *Die musikalische Instrumente in den Miniaturen des frühen Mittelalters*, i (Leipzig, 1903).

Can, H. 'Türk musikisi usulleri ve vuruoluşlari' (Time signatures and rhythms in Turkish music), *Musici mecmuasi*, nos. 261–2 (1970), 15–18.

Carl Gregor, Herzog zu Mecklenburg *Aegyptische Rhythmik: Rhythmen und Rhythmusinstrumente in heutigen Aegypten* (Strasbourg, 1960)

Carni-Cohen, D. 'An Investigation into the Tonal Structure of the Maqamat', *Journal of the International Folk Music Council*, xvi (1964), 102–6.

Caron, N. and Safvate, D. *Iran : les traditions musicales* (Paris, 1966).

Caton, M. *The Kamanche Style of Ustad Faydullah of the Province of Gilan, Iran* (MA diss., U. of California, Los Angeles, 1971).

Caton, M. 'The Vocal Ornament Takīyah in Persian Music', *Selected Reports in Ethnomusicology*, ii/1 (1974), 43–53.

Caussin, de Perceval, M. A. 'Notices anecdotiques sur les principaux musiciens arabes des trois premiers siècles de l'Islamisme', *Journal asiatique*, series 7, ii (1873), 397–596.

Cavazzi, P. *Relation historique de l'ethiopie occidentale* (Paris, 1732).

Centlivres, M., Centlivres, P. and Slobin, M. 'A Muslim Shaman of Afghan Turkestan', *Ethnology*, x (1971), 160–73.

Chabrier, J. C. 'Music in the Fertile Crescent: Lebanon, Syria, Iraq', *Cultures*, i/3 (1975), 35–58.

Bibliography

Chakravarthi, S. C. 'A Cultural Survey of Rajasthan Folk Entertainment', *Sangeet Natak*, no. 2 (1954).

Chilesotti, O. 'Le scale arabico-persana e indù', *Sammelbände der Internationalen Musikgesellschaft*, iii (1901–2), 595–8.

Chottin, A. 'Airs populaires receuillis à Fès', *Hespéris*, iii (1923), 275; iv (1924), 225.

Chottin, A. 'La musique marocaine', *France-Outre-Mer*, (1929).

Chottin, A. 'Les genres dans la musique marocaine', *Revue musicale du Maroc* (1930).

Chottin, A. *Corpus de musique marocaine*, i; *Nouba de Ochchak* (Paris, 1931).

Chottin, A. 'Les visages de la musique marocaine', *Le ménestrel*, xciii (1931), 217, 230.

Chottin, A. 'Airs populaires marocains', *Le ménestrel,*, xciv (1932), 351, 359, 367.

Chottin, A. 'Chants et danses berbères au Maroc', *Le ménestrel*, xcv (1933), 359.

Chottin, A. *Corpus de musique marocaine*, ii; *Musique et denses berberes du pays chleuh* (Paris, 1933).

Chottin, A. 'Instruments, musique et danse chleuhs', *Zeitschrift für vergleichende Musikwissenschaft*, i (1933), 11.

Chottin, A. 'La pratique du chant chez les musiciens marocains', *Zeitschrift für vergleichende Musikwissenschaft*, i (1933), 52.

Chottin, A. 'Yâ Asafâ, complainte arabe sur la perte de l'Andalousie', *Zeitschrift für vergleichende Musikwissenschaft*, iii (1935), 83.

Chottin, A. 'Chants et danses berbères; *Revue de musicologie*, xx (1936).

Chottin, A. *La musique arabe en Orient et en Occident* (Paris, 1936).

Chottin, A. 'Le chant et la danse berbères dans le folklore européen', *Proceedings of the 1st International Congress of Folklore, Tours, 1938*, 154.

Chottin, A. *Tableau de la musique morocaine* (Paris, 1939).

Chottin, A. 'La musique musulmane', *La Musique des origines à nos jours*, ed. N. Dufourcq (Paris, 1946), 74–82.

Chottin, A. 'Visages de la musique marocaine', *Encyclopédie coloniale et maritime*, iv (Paris, 1949).

Chottin, A. 'Panegyriques religieuses populaires dans la religion musulmane', in **Porte** i (1968).

Christensen, D. 'Kurdische Brautlieder aus dem Vikyet Hakkari, Süd-Ost Türkei', *Journal of the International Folk Music Council*, xiii (1961), 70–2.

Christensen, D. 'Die Musik der Kurden', *Mitteilungen der Berliner Gesellschaft für Anthropologie, Ethnologie und Urgeschichte*, i (1967), 113–19.

Christensen, D. 'Volks- und Hochkunst in der Vokalmusik der Kurden', *Volks- und Hochkunst in Dichtung und Musik : Tagunsbericht eines Colloquius, das vom 19. bis 22. Oktober 1966 am Musikwissenschaftlichen Institut der Universität des Saarlandes in Saarbrucken stattgefunden hat* (Witterschlick bei Bonn, 1968).

Christianovwitsch, A. *Esquisse historique de la musique arabe aux temps anciens* (Cologne, 1863).

Collangettes, X. M. 'Etude sur la musique arabe', *Journal asiatique* iv (1904), 365–422; viii (1906), 149–90.

Closson, E. 'Les mélodies liturgiques syriennes et chaldéennes', *La vie et les arts liturgiques*, no. 134 (1926), 178.

Comettant, O. *La musique, les musiciens et les instruments de musique chez les différents peuples du monde* (Paris, 1869).

Cowl, C. 'The Risâla fî hubr tâ'lif al-'alhan of Ja'qûb ibn ishâg al-Kindi (790–874)', *The Consort*, xxiii (1966), 129–66.

Daniel, F. Salvador *La musique arabe, ses rapports avec la musique et le chant grégorien* (Algiers, 1863).

Daniel, F. Salvador *La musique arabe* (Algiers, 1893, rev. 2/1915) (Second revised edition with notes, memoir, bibliography and music examples by H. G. Farmer).

Daniélou, A. *Catalogue of Indian Music* (Paris, 1952).

Daniélou, A. *Inde de Nord (les traditions musicales)* (Paris, 1966).

Daniélou, A. *Ragas of Northern Indian Music* (London, 1968).

Darmsteter, J. *Chants populaires des Afghans* (Paris, 1880–90).

Darmsteter, J. 'Afghan Songs', *Selected Essays* (Boston, 1895), 105.

Davidson, H. G. 'Recent Musical Progress in Egypt', *Musical Courier* (1932).

Delphin, H. and Guin, L. *Notes sur la poésie et la musique arabes dans le Maghreb algérien* (Paris, 1886).

Denys, P., Derwil, G. and Essafi 'Chansons marocaines', *Revue méditerranée* (June, 1932).

Desprez, A. 'La musique dramatique en Perse', *Revue et gazette musicale de Paris*, xl (1873), 236.

Deva, B. Chaitanya *An Introduction to Indian Music* (New Delhi, 1973).

Deva, B. Chaitanya 'Classification of Indian Musical Instruments', *Journal of the Indian Musicological Society*, iv/1 (1973), 33–45.

Didenico, S. *V pomoshch' muzïkal'nomu masteru* (To help the music master) (Tashkent, 1953).

al-Din, S.: *Bahjat al Ruh'* (Teheran, 1965).

Diószegi, V. 'Libation Songs of the Altaic Turks', *Acta ethnographica*, xix (1970), 95–106.

Donastia, J. A. de and J. Tomás 'Instrumentos de música popular española: terminología general: ensayo de clasificación', *Anuario musical*, ii (1947), 105.

Duchensne-Guillemin, M. 'La harpe à plectre iranienne: son origine et sa diffusion', *Journal of Near Eastern Studies*, xxviii (1969), 109–15.

Dufourcq, N. *La musique. Les hommes, les instruments les oeuvres* (Paris, 1965).

Duning, J. *La musique traditionnelle en Iran* (Teheran, 1974).

Dzhudzhev, S. *Bŭlgarskata narodna muzika* (Bulgarian folk music) (Sofia, 1970).

Ecker, L. E. *Arabischer, provenzalischer und deutscher Minnesang : ein motivgeschichtliche Untersuchung* (Berne and Leipzig, 1934).

Elsner, J. 'Die Prinzipien arabischer Musizierpraxis', *Jahrbuch für musikalische Volks- und Völkerkunde*, iii (1967), 90–95, 138–41.

Elsner, J. 'Remarks on the Big Argul', *Yearbook of the International Folk Music Council*, i (1969), 234–9.

Elsner, J. 'Zum Problem des Maqâm, *Gesellschaft für Musikforschung Kongressbericht, Leipzig 1966* (Kassel, 1970), 535–46.

Elsner, J. *Der Begriff des Maqâm in Ägypten in neurer Zeit* (Leipzig, 1973).

Elsner, J. 'Zur Problem des maqâm', *Acta musicologica*, xlvii (1975), 208–39.

Emsheimer, E. Über das Vorkommen und die Anwendungsart der Maultrommel in Sibirien und Zentralasien', *Ethnos*, vi (1941), 109–27.

Emsheimer, E. *Music of the Mongols* (Stockholm, 1943).

Emsheimer, E. 'Musikethnographische Bibliographie der nichtslavische Völker in Russland', *Acta musicologica*, xv (1943), 34.

The Encyclopaedia of Islam (Leiden, 1913–38, rev. 2/1954–).

Erlanger, R. d' *Melodie tunisienne* (Paris, 1937).

Erlanger, R. d' *La musique arabe* (Paris, 1930–59).

Erlanger, R. d' 'La musique arabe', *Revue musicale*, xiii/no. 128 (1932).

Ettinghausen, R. *Turkish Miniatures from the 13th to the 18th Century* (Paris, 1965).

Euba, A. 'Islamic Musical Culture among the Yoruba: a Preliminary Survey', *Essays on Music and History in Africa*, ed. K. P. Wachsmann (Evanston, 1971), 171–81.

Eykhgorn, A. *Muzykal'no etnograficheski materialy* (Musical-ethnographical materials) (Tashkent, 1963).

Eyüboğlu, I. Z. 'Karadeniz Türkülerinde ses değişmeleri' (Variations of Turkish songs in the Black Sea area), *Türk folklor araştırmalari*, no. 238 (1969), 5281–3; no. 239 (1969), 5503–7.

Ezgi, S. *Amêlî ve Nazarî Türk Musikisi* (Practice and theory of Turkish music) (1940–53).

Farah, G. *Methode de luth oriental* (Beyrouth, 1956) (in Arabic).

Farhat, H. 'Persian Classical Music', *Festival of Oriental Music and Related Arts* (Los Angeles, 1960).

Farhat, H. *The Dastgah Concept in Persian Music* (diss., U. of California, Los Angeles, 1965).

Farhat, H. *The Traditional Art Music of Iran* (Teheran, 1973).

Farmer, H. G. *The Arabian Influence on Musical Theory* (London, 1925).

Farmer, H. G. 'The Arabic Musical Manuscripts in the Bodleian Library', *Journal of the Royal Asiatic Society* (1925), 639–54.

Farmer, H. G. 'Clues for the Arabian Influence on European Musical Theory', *Journal of the Royal Asiatic Society* (1925), 61–80.

Farmer, H. G. 'The Influence of Music: from Arabic Sources', *Proceedings of the Musical Association*, lii (1925–6), 89–124.

Farmer, H. G. 'Ibn Khurdadhbih on Musical Instruments', *Journal of the Royal Asiatic Society* (1928), 509–18.

Farmer, H. G. *A History of Arabian Music to the Thirteenth Century* (London, 1929/R1973).

Farmer, H. G. 'The Congress of Arabian Music (Cairo, 1932)', *Transactions of the Glasgow Oriental Society*, vi (1929–33), 61–7.

Farmer, H. G. *Historical Facts for the Arabian Musical Influence* (London, 1930/R1970).

Farmer, H. G. 'The Origin of the Arabian Lute and Rebec', *Journal of the Royal Asiatic Society* (1930), 767–83.

Farmer, H. G. 'The Influence of Al-Farabi's "Ihsa al'ulum" (*De scientis*) on the Writers on Music in Western Europe', *Journal of the Royal Asiatic Society* (1932), 561–92.

Farmer, H. G. 'A Further Arabic-Latin Writing on Music', *Journal of the Royal Asiatic Society* (1933), 307–22.

Farmer, H. G. *Al-Farabi's Arabic–Latin Writings on Music* (London, 1934/R1965).

Farmer, H. G. 'A Maghribi Work on Musical Instruments', *Journal of the Royal Asiatic Society* (1935), 339–53.

Farmer, H. G. 'The Lute Scale of Avicenna', *Journal of the Royal Asiatic Society* (1937), 339–53.

Farmer, H. G. 'Was the Arabian and Persian Lute Fretted', *Journal of the Royal Asiatic Society* (1937), 453–60.

Farmer, H. G. 'The Instruments of Music on the Tāq-i Bustan Bas-Reliefs', *Journal of the Royal Asiatic Society* (1938), 397–412.

Farmer, H. G. 'The Structure of the Arabian and Persian Lute in the Middle Ages', *Journal of the Royal Asiatic Society* (1939), 41–51.

Farmer, H. G. *Studies in Oriental Musical Instruments*, 1st and 2nd series (London, 1931; Glasgow, 1939).

Farmer, H. G. *The Sources of Arabian Music* (Bearsden, 1940, rev. 2/1965) (A comprehensive bibliography of Arabic writings on Arabic music).

Farmer, H. G. *Sa'adyah Gaon on the Influence of Music* (London, 1943).

Farmer, H. G. '"Ghosts": an Excursus on Arabic Musical Bibliographies', *Isis*, civ (1946), 123–9.

Farmer, H. G. 'The Religious Music of Islam', *Journal of the Royal Asiatic Society* (1952), 60–65.

Farmer, H. G. *Oriental Studies: Mainly Musical* (London, 1953).

Farmer, H. G. 'The Music of Ancient Mesopotamia', 'The Music of Ancient Egypt', 'The Music of Islam', *The New Oxford History of Music*, i *Ancient and Oriental Music* (London, 1957), 228–54; 255–82; 421–78.

Farmer, H. G. *Islam: Musikgeschichte in Bildern iii/2* (Leipzig, 1966).

Farr, C. E. *The Turkoman Instrumental Music of Northern Iran* (MA diss., U. of Washington, 1972).

al-Faruqi, L. I. 'Muwashshah, a Vocal Form in Islamic Culture', *Ethnomusicology*, xix (1975), 1–29.

al-Fasì, M. *Chants anciens des femmes des Fes* (Seghers, 1967).

Fath Ali Shah *Tarikh-e Azudi*, i and ii (Teheran, 1954–5), iii, *Musik-e Iran*, nos. 89–97 (October 1959–June 1960).

Féline, P. *Arts maghrebins, musique arabesque. l'Islam et l'Occident* (Marseille, 1947).

Födemayr, F. 'Die Musik der Touareg', *Jahrbuch für musikalische Volks- und Völkerkunde*, v (1970).

Foley, R. *Songs of the Arab. the Religious Ceremonies, Shrines, and Folk Music of the Holy Christian Arab* (New York, 1953).

Fox Strangways, A. H. *Music of Hindostan* (Oxford, 1914).

Frndić, N. *Muslimanske junačke pjesma* (Moslem heroic songs) (Zagreb, 1969).

Fück, J. '"Arabische" Musikkultur und Islam', *Orientalische Literaturzeitung*, xlviii (1953).

Fürst, H. 'Musiques persanes', *Revue musicale*, vii/5 (1925–6), 228–35.

Furness, C. J. 'Communal Music among Arabians and Negroes', *Musical Quarterly*, xvi (1930), 38–51.

Galpin, F. W. 'The Sumerian Harp of Ur c. 3500 B.C.', *Music and Letters*, x (1929), 108–23.

Galpin, F. W. *Music of the Sumerians and their Immediate Successors the Babylonians and Assyrians* (Cambridge, 1937, 2/1955/R1970).

Galpin, F. W. *A Textbook of European Musical Instruments* (London, 1937).

García Barriuso, P. 'La música classica de Al-Andalus las Nubas', *Africa*, no. 26 (Madrid, 1944), 23–6.

García Barriuso, P. *La música hispano-musulmana en Marruecos* (Madrid, 1950).

Gasanov, G., ed. *Dagestanskie narodnye pesni* (Folksongs of Daghestan) (Moscow, 1959).

Gaster, T. H. *Thespis: Ritual, Myth and Drama in the Ancient Near East* (New York, 1950).

Gastoué, A. 'L'Arménie et son art traditionnel', *Revue de musicologie*, x (1929), 194–8.

Gastoué, A. 'La musique byzantine', *La musique des origines à nos jours*, ed. N. Dufourcq (Paris, 1946), 69–73.

Gastoué, A. 'La musique byzantine', in **Lavignac and de la Laurencie** (1921–31).

Gaudefroy-Demombynes, J. 'Musiques européennes le peuple arabe', *Revue de psychologie des peuples*, xi (1956), 379.

Gauthier, A. 'Résurgences sumériennes, babyloniennes et égyptiennes dans la musique occidentale', in **Porte**, i (1968), 320–22.

Gavazzi, M. 'Die Namen der altslavischen Musikinstrumente', *Volksmusik Südosteuropas*, ed. W. Wünsch (Munich, 1966), 34–49.

Gazimihâl, M. R. *Türk Nefesli Çalgilari* (Ankara, 1975).

Geiringer, K. 'Vorgeschichte und Geschichte der europäischen Laute bis zum Beginn der Neuzeit', *Zeitschrift für Musikwissenschaft*, x (1927–8), 560–603.

Geiser, B. 'Das Hackbrett in der Schweiz'.

Gerson-Kiwi, E. 'Migrations and Mutations of Oriental Folk Instruments', *Journal of the International Folk Music Council*, iv (1952), 16–19.

Gerson-Kiwi, E. *The Persian Doctrine of Dastgah-Composition* (Tel-Aviv, 1963).

Gerson-Kiwi, E. 'Women's Songs from the Yemen, their Tonal Structure and Form', *The Commonwealth of Music* (New York, 1965), 97–103.

Gerson-Kiwi, E. 'The history of the 'ud and of the tanbur', *Tatzlil*, x (1970), 46–9.

Gerson-Kiwi, E. 'On the Technique of Arab Taqsim Composition', *Musik als Gestalt und Erlebnis: Festschrift Walter Graf* (Vienna, 1970), 66–73.

Gerson-Kiwi, E. 'The Near Eastern Influence on Western Music of the 19th and 20th Centuries', *Tatzlil*, xii (1972), 14–19 (English summary).

Giorgetti, F. F. 'Zande Harp Music', *African Music*, iii/4 (1965), 74–6.

Gironcourt, G. de 'Recherche de géographie musicale dans le sud tunésien', *La géographie*, i/2 (1939), 65.

Gladwin, F. 'An Essay on Persian Music', *New Asiatic Miscellany*, i (1789), 261.

Gosvami, O. *The Story of Indian Music* (Bombay, 1957).

Grame, T. C. 'Music in the Jma al-Fna of Marrakesh', *Musical Quarterly*, lvi (1970), 74–87.

Grame, T. C. 'The Symbolism of the 'ud', *Asian Music*, iii (1972), 25–34.

Grasserie, R. de la 'Rhythmics of the Arabian and Mussulman Nations', *Babylonian and Oriental Record* (1891), 325, (1892), 62, 78, 110, 133.

Bibliography

Griaule, M. 'Symbolisme des tambours soucanais', *Mélanges d'histoire et d'esthetique musicales, offerts à Paul-Marie Masson* (Paris, 1955), 79.

Grosset, J. 'Inde: histoire de la musique depuis l'origine jusqu'à nos jours', in **Lavignac and de la Laurencie** (1921–31).

Gulik, R. H. van *The Lore of the Chinese Lute* (Tokyo, 1940) (Addenda et Corrigenda, Tokyo, 1951).

Günther, R., ed. *Musikkulturen Asiens, Afrikas und Ozeaniens im 19. Jahrhundert* (Regensburg, 1973).

Hacobian, Z. 'L'improvisation et l'ornematation en Orient et en Occident', *Journal of the International Folk Music Council*, xiv (1964), 74–6.

Hage, L. *Musique occidentale et orientale* (Kaslik, 1973).

Hai, T. Q. 'Bibliographie: musique iranienne', *Bulletin du Centre d'Études de Musique Orientale*, x–xi (1972), 43–8.

Halim, A. 'Music and Musicians of Shah Jahan's Court', *Islamic Culture*, xix (1945).

Hanna, S. A. '*Al-jawārī al-mughanniyāt*: the Singing Arab Maids', *Southern Folklore Quarterly*, xxxiv (1970), 325–30.

Hartmann, H. *Die Musik der Sumerischen Kultur* (Frankfurt am Main, 1960).

Hartmann, M. *Metrum und Rhythmus: die Entstehung des arabischen Versmasses* (Giessen, 1896).

Hartmann, M. 'Arabische Lieder aus Syrien', *Zeitschrift der Deutschen morgenländischen Gesellschaft* (1897), 177.

Hause, H. E. 'Terms for Musical Instruments in the Sudanic Languages', suppl. 7 to the *Journal of the American Oriental Society*, lxviii/1 (1948).

Haydamaka, L. 'Koizba-bandura: National Ukrainian Musical Instrument', *Guitar Review*, iii (1970), 13–18.

el-Hefny, M. *Ibn Sina's Musiklehre* (diss., Berlin Univ., 1931).

el-Hefny, M. 'Music in Egypt', *Egypt in 1945* (Calcutta, 1946), 218.

el-Hefny, M. *Aegyptische Musik von einst bis heute* (Cairo, 1956).

Heinitz, W. 'Ein Materialbeitrag zur Kenntnis der arabischen Musik', *Zeitschrift für Musikwissenschaft*, iv (1922), 193–8.

Helfritz, H. 'Muziekbeoefening in Arabië', *De Muziek*, v (1931), 145.

Hickmann, E. 'La musique magique, rituelle et cultuelle des Égyptiens pharaoniques', in **Porte**, i (1968), 310–19.

Hickmann, H. 'Un instrument a cordes inconnu de l'époque copte', *Bulletin de la Société d' Archéologie copte*, xii (1946–7), 63–80.

Hickmann, H. *La trompette dans l'Egypte ancienne* (Cairo, 1946).

Hickmann, H. *Terminologie arabe des instruments de musique* (Cairo, 1947).

Hickmann, H. 'La cliquette, instrument de percussion de l'époque copte', *Bulletin de la Société d'Archéologie copte*, xiii (1950), 1–12.

Hickmann, H. 'La daraboukkah', *Bulletin de l'Institut d'Egypte*, xxxiii (1951–2), 229–45.

Hickmann, H. 'La musique polyphonique dans l'Egypte ancienne', *Bulletin de l'Institut d'Egypte*, xxxiv (1952), 229–44.

Hickmann, H. 'Les harpes de l'Egypte Pharaonique', *Bulletin de l'Institut de l'Egypte*, xxxv (1953), 309–78.

Hickmann, H. 'Le problème notation musicale dans l'Egypt ancienne', *Bulletin de l'Institut d'Egypte*, xxxvi (1955), 489–531.

Hickmann, H. *45 siècles de musique dans l'Egypte ancienne à travers la sculpture, la peinture, l'instrument* (Paris, 1956).

Hickmann, H. *Aegypten: Musikgeschichte in Bildern*, ii/1 (Leipzig, 1961).

Hickmann, H. 'Pharaonic Jingles', *The Commonwealth of Music* (New York, 1965), 45–70.

Hickmann, H. 'Die Musik des arabish islamischen Bereichs', *Handbuch der Orientalistik*, i (1970), 1–134.

Hickmann, H. and Carl Gregor, Herzog zu Mecklenburg *Catalogue d'enregistrements de musique folklorique égyptienne* (Baden-Baden, 1957).

Hoerburger, F. *Folksmusik in Afghanistan* (Regensburg, 1969).

Hoerburger, F. 'Stilschichten der Musik in Afghanistan und ihre gegenseitige Durchdringung', *Musik als Gestalt und Erlebnis: Festschrift Walter Graf* (Vienna, 1970), 92–101.

Hoerburger, F. 'Supplementary Jingling in the Instrumental Folk Music of Afghanistan', *Journal of the International Folk Music Council*, xx (1968), 51–4.

Hofmann, S. 'Essential Aspects of Arabian Music', *New Outlook, Middle East Monthly*, i (1957).

Hofmann, S. 'La musique arabe en Israel: sa preservation, sa renovation', *Journal of the International Folk Music Council*, xvi (1964), 25–8.

Hofmann, S. 'The Destiny of a Yemenite Folk Tune', *Journal of the International Folk Music Council*, xx (1968), 25–9.

Hornbostel, E. M. von 'Notizen ueber kirgisische Musikinstrumente und Melodien, *Unter Kirgisen und Turkmenen*, ed. R. Karutz (Leipzig, 1911), 196–218.

Hornbostel, E. M. von 'Zum Kongress für arabische Musik, Kairo 1932', *Zeitschrift für vergleichende Musikwissenschaft*, i (1933), 25.

Hornbostel, E. M. von and Lachmann, R. 'Asiatische Parallelen zur Berbermusik', *Zeitschrift für vergleichende Musikwissenschaft*, i (1933), 4.

Hornbostel, E. M. von and Sachs, C. 'Classification of Musical Instruments', *Galpin Society Journal*, xiv (1961), 3–29.

Huart, C. 'Musique persane', in **Lavignac and de le Laurencie** (1921–31).

Huart, C. 'Étude biographique sur trois musiciens arabes', *Journal Asiatique*, 8th series, no. 3 (1884), 141.

Humeniuk, A. I. *Ukrains'ki narodni muzychni instrumenty* (Ukrainian folk musical instruments) (Kiev, 1967).

Husmann, H. *Grundlagen der antiken und orientalischen Musikkultur* (Berlin, 1961).

Husmann, H. 'Antike und Orient in ihren Bedeutung für die europäische Musik', *Gesellschaft für Musikforschung Kongressbericht, Hamburg 1956* (Kassel and Basel, 1957), 24–32.

Husmann, H. 'Arabische Maqamen in ostsyrischer Kirchenmusik', *Musik als Gestalt und Erlebnis: Festschrift Walter Graf* (Vienna, 1970), 102–8.

Huth, A. *Die Musikinstrumente Ost-Turkistans* (diss., Berlin Univ., 1928).

Idelsohn, A. Z. 'Die Moqamen der arabischen Musik', *Sammelbände der Internationalen Musikgesellschaft*, xv (1913–14), 11.

Idelsohn, A. Z. *Hebräish-Orientalischer Melodienschatz* (Leipzig, 1914–32).

Idelsohn, A. Z. *Phonographierte Gesänge und Aussprachsproben des Hebräischen der jemenitischen, persischen und syrischen Juden* (Vienna, 1917).

al-Ikhtiyār, N. *al-Fūlklūr al-Ghinā 'I 'ind al-'Arab* (Arab folksong) (Damascus, c1968).

Ilerici, K. *Türk müziçi ve armonisi* (Turkish music and harmony) (Istanbul, 1970).

Indian Musical and Noise Making Instruments, Denver Art Museum, leaflet series xxix (1931).

Ismail, M. 'Traditional Music in the Sudan', *Notes on Education and Research in African Music*, no. 1 (July, 1967), 17–25.

Jairazbhoy, N. A. 'L'Islam en Inde et au Pakistan', in **Porte**, i (1968), 454–63 'A Preliminary Survey of the Oboe in India', *Ethnomusicology*, xiv (1970), 375–88.

Jairazbhoy, N. A. *The Ragas of North Indian Music, Their Structure and Evolution* (London, 1971).

Jargy, S. *La musique arabe* (Paris, 1971).

Jeannin, Dom J. 'Le chant lithurgique syrien', *Journal asiatique*, (1912), 295 (1913), 65.

Jeannin, Dom J. *Mélodies lithurgiques syriennes et chaldéennes* (Paris, 1924).

Jeannin, Dom J. 'L'Octoechos syrien', *Oriens christianus*, n.s. 3, iii (1928), 82, 277.

Jenkins, J. *Musical Instruments* (London, 1958, 2/1970).

Jenkins, J., ed. *Ethnic Musical Instruments: Identification—Conservation* (London, 1970).

Jones, L. J. *The Persian Santur: a Description of the Instrument, together with an Analysis of the Four Dastgah* (MA diss., U. of Washington, 1971).

Kačulev, I. 'Bŭlgarski dvuglasni narodni muzikalni instrumenti' (Bulgarian two-part folk instruments), *Bŭlgarska muzika*, xxi/4 (1970), 27–33.

Kačulev, I. 'Bulgarian Folk Instruments', *Viltis*, xxix/3 (1970), 8–10.

Karelova, I. N., ed. *Voprosy muzykal'noĭ kul'tury Uzbekistana* (Matters concerning the musical culture of Uzbekistan) (Tashkent, 1969).

Karomatov, F. M. 'O lokal'nykh stiliakh uzbekskoĭ narodnoĭ muzyki' (On local styles of Uzbek folk music), *Muzyka narodov Azii i Afrika* (Folk music of Asia and Africa), V. S. Vinogradov, ed. (Moscow, 1969), 35–49 (Eng. trans. 'On the Regional Styles of Uzbek Music', *Asian Music*, iv/1 (1972), 48–58).

Karomatov, F. M. *Uzbekskaia instrumental'naia muzyka* (Uzbek musical instruments) (Tashkent, 1972).

Karpati, J. 'Melodie, vers et structure strophique dans la musique berbère (imazighen) du Maroc central', *Studia musicologica*, i (1961), 451–73.

Kaufman, N. 'Pesni na bŭlgarite makhamedani ot Rodopite' (Songs of Mohammedan Bulgarians of Rhodope), *Rodopski sbornik*, ii (1969), 41–130 (English and Russian summaries).

Kaufmann, W. *Musical Notations of the Orient; Notational Systems of Continental, East, South and Central Asia* (Bloomington, 1967).

Kaxim, U. *Musiki istilhati* (Ankara, 1964).

Kazakhskie Sovetskie Narodnye Pesni (Kazakh soviet folk songs) (Alma Ata, 1959).

Kel'dysh, G. V., ed. *Entsiklopedichesky muzykal'ny slover* (Musical encyclopaedic dictionary) (Moscow, 1959).

Khaldun, Ibn *The Muqqadimah* (London, 1958) (trans. F. Rosenthal).

Khatschi, K. *Der Dastgah: Studien zur neuen, persischen Musik* (Regensburg, 1962).

Khatschi, K. 'Das Intervalsbildungsprinzip des persischen Dastgāh Shur', *Jahrbuch für musikalsche Volks- und Völkerkunde*, iii (1967), 70–84, 128–33.

Khavas, El'-Said M. A. *Sovremenaia arabskaia narodnaia pesnia* (Contemporary Arabian folksongs) (Moscow, 1970).

Khé, T. V. 'La musique iranienne', *Bulletin du Centre d'Étude de Musique Orientale*, x–xi (1972), 16–28.

Kiesewetter, R. G. *Die Musik der Araber* (Leipzig, 1842).

Kilner, A. D. 'The Strings of Musical Instruments: their Names, Numbers, and Significance', *Studies in Honor of Benno Landsberger on his Seventy-Fifth Birthday April 21, 1965* (Chicago, 1965), 261–72.

Kinsky, G. 'Doppelrohrblatt-instrumente mit Windkapsel', *Archiv für Musikwissenschaft*, vii (1925), 253–96.

Kishibe, S. 'Emigration of Musicians from Central Asia to China and Diffusion of Western Music in China', *Annales of the Institute of History, Faculty of General Culture, Tokyo University*, no. 1 (1953).

Klichkova, V. 'Narodni muzichki instrumenti u Makedonije' (Folk music instruments of Macedonia), (Belgrade, 1960), 225–32 (Congress of Yugoslav Folklorists at Zajechar and Negotina, 1958).

Knosp, G. 'Notes sur la musique persane', *Guide musicale*, iv (1909), 283, 307, 327, 347.

Koizumi, F. 'Turkey no gakufu' (The notation of Turkish music), *Philharmony*, xliv/2 (Tokyo, 1972), 8–14.

Komitas 'La musique rustique arménienne', *Revue musicale mensuelle* (1907), 472.

Kothari, K. S. *Indian Folk Musical Instruments* (New Delhi, 1968).

Kontev, P. and M. 'Folk Dance Instruments: Gadulka', *The Folklorist*, iv (1957–8), 111.

Kontev, P. and M. 'Folk Dance Instruments: Kaval', *The Folklorist*, iv (1957–8), 12.

Kretzenbacher, L. 'Südosteuropäische Primitivinstrumente vom "Rummelpott"-typ in vergleichendmusikvolkskundlicher Forschung', *Volksmusik Südeuropas*, ed. W. Wünsch (Munich, 1966), 50–97.

Krishnaswami, V. S. 'Research on Musical Instruments of India', *Journal of the Music Academy, Madras*, xxxiii (1962), 101–10.

Krishnaswami, V. S. *Musical Instruments of India* (Boston, 1965, 2/1971).

Krishnaswami, V. S. 'Drums of India through the Ages', *The Journal of the Music Academy, Madras*, xxxviii (1967), 72–82.

Krishnaswami, V. S. 'Musical Instruments of India', *Asian Music*, ii/2 (1971), 31–42.

Krohn, I. 'Mongolische Melodien', *Zeitschrift für Musikwissenschaft*, iii (1920), 65.

Kuckertz, J. 'Origin and Development of the Rabab', *Sangeet Natak*, xv (1970), 16–30.

Kuckertz, I. 'Melody Formation in the Middle East, India, and South-east Asia', *Bulletin of the Ramakrishna Mission Institute of Culture*, xiv/3 (Calcutta, 1973), 86–91.

Kulakovsky, L. V. *Pesnya, ee yazyk, struktura, sudby* (Song, its language, structure, destiny—based on material from Russian and Ukrainian folk and Soviet popular song) (Moscow, 1962).

Kümmel, H. M. 'Zur Stimmung der babylonischen Harfe', *Orientalia*, xxxix (1970), 152–63.

Kunst, J. 'Musicological Exploration in the Indian Archipelago', *The Asiatic Review* (October 1936).

Kunst, J. *Music in Java: its History, its Theory, and its Technique* (The Hague, 1949, rev. 2/).

Kunst, J. *Ethnomusicology* (The Hague, 1950, rev. 3/1959).

Kunst, J. *Cultural Relations between Balkans and Indonesia* (Amsterdam, 1954).

Kutahialian, J. O. *Ecriture musicale arabe moderne* (Marseilles, 1957).

Lach, R. 'Musik im Islam', *Der Auftakt*, i (1920–21), 282.

Lach, R. *Gesänge russicher Kriegsgefangener* (Vienna, 1926–52).

Lachmann, R. *Die Musik in den tunesischen Städten* (diss., Berlin Univ., 1922) *Archiv für Musikwissenschaft*, v (1923), 136–71.

Lachmann, R. 'Ein grundlegendes Werk über die Musik Indiens', *Archiv für Musikwissenschaft*, vi (1924), 484.

Lachmann, R. 'Ostturkestanische Gesänge', *Von Land und Leuten in Ostturkestan*, ed. A. von Lecoq (Leipzig, 1928).

Lachmann, R. *Musik des Orients* (Breslau, 1929).

Lachmann, R. 'Musikwissenschaftliche Forschungen in Tunesien', *Forschungen und Fortschritte*, vi (1930).

Lachmann, R. 'Musikalische Forschungsaufgaben im vorderen Orient', *Bericht über die 1. Sitzung der Gesellschaft zur Erforschung der Musik des Orients am 27. April 1930* (Berlin, 1930), 3.

Lachmann, R. 'Von der Kunstmusik des vorderen Orients', *Kultur und Schallplatte*, ii (1931), 164.

Lachmann, R. 'Asiatische Parallelen zur Berbermusik', *Zeitschrift für vergleichende Musikwissenschaft*, i (1933), 4.

Lachmann, R. 'Das indische Tonsystem bei Bharata und sein Ursprung', *Zeitschrift für vergleichende Musikwissenschaft*, i (1933), 73.

Lachmann, R. 'Mustaqbil al-mūsiqa l-'arabijja', *Al Kullija l-'arabija*, xvi/1 (1935), 17.

Lachmann, R. and Hefney, M. el *Ja'qūb Ishāk al-Kindi Risāla fi hubr ta' lif al-alhan* (About the composition of melodies) (Leipzig, 1931).

Lajtha, L. *A tárogató utja Persziából Európába* (Migration of the tárogató from Persia to Europe) (Budapest, 1923).

Lajtha, L. 'Két régi lantról' (Of two lutes), *Zenei szemle*, xi/3–5 (1927).

Land, J. P. N. 'Tonschriftversuche und Melodien Proben aus dem muhammedanischen Mittelalter', *Vierteljahrschrift für Musikwissenschaft*, ii (1876) repr. *Sammelbände für vergleichende Musikwissenschaft*, i (1922), 77.

Land, J. P. N. 'Over de toonladders der Arabische muziek', *Verslagen en Mededelingen van de Koninklijke Akademie van Wetenschappen, Afd. Letterlamde* 2nd series, ix (1880), 246.

Land, J. P. N. *Récherches sur l'histoire de la gamme arabe* (Leiden, 1884) (This work contains the section on instruments from al-Farabi's *Kitab al Musiqi al Kabir* in French and Arabic translation).

Bibliography

Land, J. P. N. 'Essais de notation musicale chez les arabes et les persans', *Études archéologiques, linguistiques et historiques dédiées à M. le Dr. C. Leemans* (Leiden, 1885), 315.

Land, J. P. N. 'Remarks on the Earliest Development of Arabic Music', *Proceedings of the 9th International Congress of Orientalists, London 1892*, ii (London, 1893), 155.

Lane, E. W. *An Account of the Manners and Customs of the Modern Egyptians* (London, 1836, 5/1871).

Lange, D. de *De collectie Indische muziekinstrumenten, bockwerken over muziek en schilderijen in het Rijks Ethnographisch Museum te Leiden* (Amsterdam, 1881).

Lange, D. de and Snellman, J. F. 'La musique et les instruments de musique dans les Indes Orientales Neerlandaises', in **Lavignac and de la Laurencie** (1921–31).

Lavignac, A. and Laurencie, L. de la *Encyclopedie de la musique et dictionnaire du Conservatoire* (Paris, 1921–31).

Ledang, O. K. 'On the Acoustics and the Systematic Classification of the Jaw's Harp', *Yearbook of the International Folk Music Council*, iv (1972), 95–103.

Lemm, F. H. 'Musique et arts nègres. Lettres du Soudan', *Bulletin des recherches soudanaises*, no. 36 (Koulouba, September, 1936).

Lens, M. T. de 'Ce que nous savons de la musique et les instruments de musique du Maroc', *Bulletin de l'Institut des Hautes Études Marocaines* (December, 1920).

Liang, T. *Chung-kuo yüeh ch'i ta kang* (Chinese musical instruments and pictures) (Taipei, 1970).

Linin, A. 'O muzičkim instrumentima makedonskih Slovena' (On the musical instruments of the Macedonian Slavs), *Zvuk*, no. 89 (1968), 519–29 (English summary).

Linin, A. 'Gajdite na balkanot' (The bagpipes in the Balkans), *Makedonski folklor*, ii (1969), 305–15.

Livermore, A. *A Short History of Spanish Music* (London, 1972).

Lloyd, A. L. 'Albanian Folk Song', *Folk Music Journal*, i (1968), 205–23.

Loret, V. 'Quelques documents relatifs à la litterature et à la musique populaires de la Haute-Egypt', *Mémoires de la Mission Archéologique Française au Caire*, i (1881–4), 305.

Loret, V. 'Les flûtes égyptiennes antiques', *Journal asiatique*, lxiv (1889), 133.

Loret, V. 'Les cymbales égyptiennes', *Sphynx*, v (1902).

Macdonald, D. B. 'Emotional Religion in Islam as Affected by Music and Singing: Being a Translation of a Book of the Ihyā 'ulūm ad-dīn of al-Ghazzāli', *Journal of the Royal Asiatic Society* (1901), 195–252, 705–48; (1905), 1.

Machabey, A. 'La musique suméro-chaldéenne et égyptienne', *La musique des origines à nos jours*, ed. N. Dufourcq (Paris, 1946), 59–62.

Mackay, M. 'Traditional Musical Instruments of Nigeria', *Niger Fld*, xv (1950), 112–32.

Macler, F. *La Musique en Arménie* (Paris, 1917).

Mahdi, S. el *La musique arabe* (Paris, 1972).

Malm, W. P. *Music Cultures of the Pacific, Near East and Asia* (Englewood Cliffs, N.J., 1967).

Mahmoud, P. *A Theory of Persian Music and its Relation to Western Practice* (diss., U. of Indiana, 1957).

Mammery, A. 'La musique et le théatre populaires à Marrakech', *L'Atlas*, special issue (1939).

Manga, J. 'A török háborúk emlékei a magyarországi szlouák népdalokban', (Reminiscences of the Turkish wars in the Slovak folksongs of Hungary), *Ethnographia, a Magyar néprajzi társaág folyôirata*, lxvii (1956), 241.

Manik, L. *Das arabische Tonsystem im Mittelalter* (Leiden, 1969).

Manniche, L. *Ancient Egyptian Musical Instruments* (Munich and Berlin, 1975).

Marcel-Dubois, C. *Les instruments de musique de l'Inde ancienne* (Paris, 1941).

Marcuse, S. *Musical Instruments: a Comprehensive Dictionary* (New York, 1964).

Mariano, P. A. 'Burmese Music and Musical Instruments', *Burma, a Handbook of Practical Information*, ed. J. G. Scott (London, 3/1921), 360.

Martens, F. H. 'The Musical Observations of a Maroccan Ambassador (1690–91)', *Musical Quarterly*, xv (1929), 574–82.

Massoudieh, M. T. *Awāz-e-Šur: zur Melodiebildung in der persischen Kunstmusik* (Regensburg, 1968).

Massoudieh, M. T. 'Die Melodie Matnawī in der persischen Kunstmusik', *Orbis musicae*, i (1971), 57–66.

Massoudieh, M. T. 'Hochzeitslieder aus Balucestari', *Jahrbuch für musikalische Volks und Völkerkunde*, vii (1973).

Massoudieh, M. T. 'Tradition und Wandel in der persischen Musik des 19. Jahrhundert', *Musikkulturen Asiens, Afrikas und Ozeaniens im 19. Jahrhundert*, ed. R. Günther (Regensburg, 1973), 73–96.

Matchinsky, A. 'A propos de la gamme musicale égyptienne', *Publication du Musée de l'Hermitage*, ii (1935), 9.

Matas, M. G. 'Instrumentos musicales folklóricos de España', *Anuario musical*, xi (1956), 123–64.

Mauguin, B. *Musique meuleui, musique sacrée* (Konya, 1965).

Mauguin, B. 'L'appel à la prière dans l'Islam', in **Porte**, i (1968), 404–8.

Mauguin, B. 'Musique de mosquée et de Confrérie en Turquie', in **Porte**, i (1968) 422–40.

McGowan, K. 'Music and Dance of Turkey', *Viltis*, xxvii/2 (Denver, 1968), 5–12.

Menemenioğlu, H. 'Kemençe hakkinda etüd' (Study of the kemençe), *Musiki mecmuasi* no. 260 (1970), 4–13.

Meny de Marangue, M. *La musique marocaine (analyses des modes; vues sur la musique populaire)* (Lyons, 1923).

Merriam, A. P. 'An Annotated Bibliography of African and African-derived Music since 1936', *Africa*, xxi (1951), 319–29.

Mersenne, M. *Harmonie universelle* (Paris, 1636 R1965; Eng. trans. of ii, *The Books on Instruments*, 1957).

Milŏsević, V. 'Prilog melografiranju muslimanskog pjevanja vjerskih tekstova u Bosni i Hercegovini' (A contribution to the transcription of Moslem religious singing in Bosnia and Herzegovina), *Zbornik krajiskih muzeja*, iii (1968–9), 141–53.

Misra, L. *Bharatiya Sangeet Vadya* (Indian musical instruments) (New Delhi, 1973).

Moheyeddin, K. 'Muslim Contribution to Indian Music', *Pakistan Review* (March, 1955).

Mokri, M. *Kurdish Songs with Transliteration, Persian Translation and Glossary* (Teheran, 1951).

Mokri, M. 'La musique sacrée des Kurdes "Fideles de vérite" en Iran', in **Porte**, i (1968).

Mondon-Vidailhet, M. 'La musique Éthiopienne' in **Lavignac and de la Laurencie** (1921–31).

Morgenstierne, G. 'Some Folk-Songs from Nuristan', *To Honor Roman Jakobson*, ii (The Hague, 1967), 1378–92.

Moule, A. C. 'A List of the Musical and other Sound Producing Instruments of the Chinese', *Journal of the North-China Branch of the Royal Asiatic Society*, xxxix (1908), 1–160.

Murko, M. *Bericht über phonographische Aufnahmen epischer, meist mohammedanischer Volkslieder im nordwestlichen Bosnien* (Vienna, 1912).

Mutatkar, S. 'A Short Account of the Development of Islamic Music', *Lakshya sangeet*, i (1954–5).

an-Nābulusī, A. *Iḍāḥ ad-dalālāt fī samā 'al-ālāt* (Clear exposition of the arguments on listening to musical instruments) (Damascus, 1885).

Nametak, A. *Od bešike do neotike: Narodne lirske i pripovijedne pjesme bosanskoher cegovackih muslimana* (From the cradle to the spade: lyric and narrative folksongs of the Moslems of Bosnia-Herzegovina) (Sarajevo, 1970).

Nasr, S. H. 'The Influence of Sufism on Traditional Persian Music', *Studies in Comparative Religion*, vi (1972), 225–34.

Nettl, B. *Reference Materials in Ethnomusicology* (Detroit, 1961).

Nettl, B. 'Attitudes towards Persian Music in Tehran, 1969', *Musical Quarterly*, lvi (1970), 183–97.

Nettl, B. *The Classical Music of Iran* (New York, 1973).

Nettl, B. 'Aspects of Form in the Instrumental Performance of the Persian *Āvāz*', *Ethnomusicology*, xviii (1974), 405–14.

Nettl, B. 'The Role of Music in Culture: Iran, a Recently Developed Nation', *Contemporary Music and Music Cultures* (Englewood Cliffs, New Jersey, 1975), 71–100.

Nettl, B. and Fotlin jr, B. *Daramad of Chahargad: a Study in the Performance Practice of Persian Music* (Detroit, 1972).

Nettl, B. and Riddle, R. 'Taqsim Nahawand; A Study of Sixteen Performances by Jihad Racy', *Yearbook of the International Folk Music Council*, v (1973), 11–50.

Neubauer, E. 'Drei "Makamen" des Asik Divani', *Orbis musicae*, i (1971), 39–56.

Nikiprowetzky, T. *Les instruments de musique au Niger* (Paris, 1963) (in English and French).

Nikiprowetzky, T. *La musique dans la vie* (Paris, 1967).

Nikiprowetzky, T. 'Traditional Music in French-Speaking Africa', *Notes on Education and Research in African Music*, no. 1 (July, 1967), 26–31.

Oliveria, E. V. de *Instrumentos musicais populares portugueses* (Lisbon, 1966).

Olsen, P. Rovsing 'Enregiedrements faits a Kuwait et a Bahrain', *Les Colloques de Wégimont, IV 1958–60: Ethnomusicology III*, (Paris, 1964), 138–169.

Olsen, P. Rovsing 'La musique africaine dans le Golfe Persique', *Journal of the International Folk Music Council*, xix (1967), 28–36.

Olsen, P. Rovsing 'Six versions de taqsim en maqan rast', *Studia Instrumentorum Musicae Popularis iii. Festschrift to Ernst Emsheimer* (Stockholm, 1974), 197–202.

Olsen, P. Rovsing 'Compte rendir d'un voyage au Moyen-Orient', *Acta musicologica*, xlvii (1975), 3–15.

Oransay, G. 'Das Tonsystem der türkei-türkischen Kunstmusik', *Die Musikforschung*, x (1957), 250–64.

Oransay, G. *Die traditionelle türkische Kunstmusik* (Ankara, 1964).

Oransay, G. *Die melodische Linie und der Begriff Makam der traditionellen türkischen Kunstmusik von 15. bis zum 19. Jahrhundert* (diss., U. of Munich, 1966; Ankara, 1966).

Özergin, M. K. 'Boru çalgisinin yayilisi' (Diffusion of trumpet-like instruments), *Türk folklor araştirmalari*, no. 260 (1971), 5894–8; no. 261 (1971), 5938–42.

Özergin, M. K. 'XVII. yüzilinda Osmanli ülkesinde çalgilar' (17th-century instruments in the Ottoman Empire), *Türk folklor araştirmalari*, no. 262 (1971), 5955–9, 6006–9, 6031–6, 6049–56.

Oztuna, Y. *Türk musikisi ansiklopedisi* (Encyclopedia of Turkish music), i (Istanbul, 1970).

Özyurt, S. *Die Türkenlieder und das Turkenbild in der deutschen Volksüberlieferung vom 16. bis zum 20. Jahrhundert* (Munich, 1972).

Pacholczyk, J. *Marcib: Regulative Principles in Koran Chant of Shaikh Abdulbasit Abdulsamat* (diss., U. of California, Los Angeles, 1970).

Panum, H. *Stringed Instruments of the Middle Ages* (London, 1939).

Parisot, J. *Rapport sur une mission scientifique en Turquie d'Asie (chants orientaux)* (Paris, 1899).

Pasini, F. 'Prolegomènes à une étude sur les sources de l'histoire musicale de l'ancienne Égypte', *Sammelbände der Internationalen Musikgesellschaft*, ix (1907–8).

Pekker, I. *V. A. Uspenskij* (His work as an ethnographer-musicologist and composer in Uzbekistan and Turkmenistan) (Moscow, 1953).

Pelagaud, F. 'Syriens et Phrygiens', in **Lavignac and de la Laurencie** (1921–31).

Percival, C. de 'Les musiciens arabes', *Journal asiatique* (1873), 397.

Picken, L. 'Instrumental Polyphonic Folk Music in Asia Minor', *Proceedings of the Royal Musical Association*, lxxx (1953–4), 73–86.

Picken, L. 'The Origin of the Short Lute', *Journal of the Galpin Society*, viii (1955), 32–42.

Picken, L. 'Central Asian Tunes in the Gagaku Tradition', *Festschrift für Walter Wiora* (Kassel, 1967), 545–51.

Picken, L. *Turkish Folk Musical Instruments* (London, 1975).

Pieper, C. 'Kunst und Musik in Tunesien', *Institut für Auslandsbeziehungen Stuttgart: Zeitschrift für Kulturaustausch*, xix (1969), 128–31.

Plumley, G. A. *El Tanbur, the Sudanese Lyre or the Nubian Kissar* (Cambridge, 1975).

Poduval, R. V. 'Music and the Muslim Courts of India', *The Madras Music Academy Annual Conference Souvenir, December 1953* (Madras, 1954).

Polak, A. J. *Die Harmonisierung indischer, türkischer und japanischer Melodien* (Leipzig, 1905).

Porte, J., ed. *Encyclopedie des musiques sacrées* (Paris, 1968).

Prajnananda, S. *A Historical Study of Indian Music* (Calcutta, 1965).

Prince, J. D. 'Muhammadan Music', *Encyclopedia of Religion and Ethics*, ed. J. Hastings, ix (Edinburgh, 1917), 53.

Pulver, J. 'The Music of Ancient Egypt', *Proceedings of the Musical Association*, xlvii (1921–2).

Qureshi, R. 'Indo-Muslim Religious Music, an Overview', *Asian Music*, iii/2 (1972), 15–22.

Rabanit, H. *Sur la musique morocaine, dans France-Islam* (October, 1924).

Rashīd, Subhi Answar 'Neue Akkadische Leierdarstellungen und ihre Bedeutung fuer die Mesopotämishce Musikgeschichte', *Journal of Archaeology in Iraq*, xxiii (1967), 144–9.

Rashīd, Subhi Answar *Tārikh al-ālat al-musiqiyya fī al-'irāq al-qadim*, (History of musical instruments in ancient Iraq) (Beirut, 1970).

Rashīd, Subhi Answar *Al-ālat al-musiqiyya fī al-'usūr al-islāmiyya*, (Musical instruments in Islamic age) (Baghdad, 1975).

Receuil des travaux du congrès de musique Arabe qui s'est tenu au Caire en 1932 (Cairo, 1934).

Regelsperger, G. 'Les instruments de musique dans le pays du Chari-Tchad', *La Nature*, xxxvii (1908), 19.

Reiche, J. P. 'Stilelemente sudtürkischer Davul-Zurna-Stücke', *Jahrbuch für musikalische Volks- und Völkerkunde*, v (1970).

Reichow, J. *Die Entfaltung eines Melodiemodells im Genus Sikah* (Regensburg, 1971).

Reinhard, K. 'Tanzlieder der Turkmenen in der Süd-Türkei', *Gesellschaft für Musikforschung Kongressbericht Hamburg, 1956* (Leipzig, 1970), 189–92.

Reinhard, K. 'Types of Turkmenian Songs in Turkey', *Journal of the International Folk Music Council*, ix (1957), 49–53.

Reinhard, K. *Die türkische Musik* (Berlin, 1962).

Reinhard, K. 'Die gegenwartige Prazis des Epengesänges in der Türkei', *Grazer und Münchener balkanologische Studien*, ed. W. Wünsch and H. J. Kissling (Munich, 1967), 83–96.

Reinhard, K. 'Die Quellensituation der türkischen Kunstmusik: Gedanke zur Frage mündlicher und schriftlicher Tradition und zum Problem Improvisation-Komposition', *Festschrift für Walter Wiora* (Kassel, 1967), 578–82.

Reinhard, K. *Turquie: les traditions musicales* (Paris, 1969).

Reinhard, K. 'Grundlagen und Ergebnisse der Erforschung türkischer Musik', *Acta musicologica*, xliv (1972), 266–80.

Reinhard, K. 'Die Turkei im 19. Jahrhundert', *Musikkulturen Asiens, Afrikas und Ozeaniens im 19. Jahrhundert*, ed. R. Günther (Regensburg, 1973), 21–49.

Reinhard, K. and Reinhard, U. *Auf der Fidel mein . . . Volkslieder von der osttürkischen Schwarzmeerküste* (Berlin, 1968).

Rezvani, M. *Le théâtre et la danse en Iran* (Paris, 1963).

Ribera, J. *La música de las Cantigas* (Madrid, 1922; Eng. trans. and abr., 1929).

Ricard, P. 'Le conservatoire de musique marocaine à Rabat', *France-Outre-Mer* (1936).

Ricard, P. *Historia de la música arabe medieval y su influencia en la española* (Madrid, 1927).

Ricard, P. *Essai d'action sur la musique et le théâtre populaire marocain* (?Rabat, 1936).

Ricard, P. 'La rénovation des arts musicaux au Maroc', *Revue d'Afrique* (1936).

Ridgeway 'Origin of the Guitar and Fiddle', *Man*, no. 7 (1908).

Rihtman, C. 'Membronofoni muzički instrumenti u narodnoj tradiciji BiH' (Membranophones in the folk tradition of Bosnia and Herzegovina), *Radova Akademije Nauka i Umjetnosti Bosne i Hercegovine*, xxxii (1967), 103–21.

Rihtman, C. 'Arhaični elementi u svatovskim pjesmama Srba i Hrvata bosanskohercegovačkog sela' (Arabic elements in the wedding songs of the Serbs and Croats of Bosni and Herzegovina), *Narodono stvaralstvo : folklor*, vii/25 (1968), 70–75 (French summary).

Rimmer, J. *Ancient Musical Instruments of Western Asia* (London, 1969).

Ritter, H. 'Mesopotamische Studien, ii: Vierzig arabische Volkslieder', *Der Islam* (1920), 120.

Robinson, A. E. 'Sudan Drums', *Man*, xxxii (1932), 259.

Robson, J. *Ancient Arabian Musical Instruments : as Described by Al-Mafuddal ibn Salama (9th Century) in the . . . 'Kitab al-malahi . . .'* (Glasgow, 1938).

Robson, J. 'Kitab al-Malahi of Abu Talib al-Mufad al ibn Salama', *Journal of the Royal Asiatic Society* (1938), 231–49 (trans. by J. Robson with an introduction by H. G. Farmer).

Roda, C. de 'Les instruments de musique en Espagne au XIIIe siècle', *Report of the 4th Congress of the International Musical Society, London 1911* (London, 1912), 332–3.

Rouanet, J. 'La chanson populaire arabe en Algérie', *Revue musicale*, v (1905), 161.

Rouanet, J. 'Esquisse pour une histoire de la musique arabe en Algérie', *Mercure musicale*, i (1905), 553 ; ii (1906), 128, 208.

Rouanet, J. 'La musique arabe' and 'La musique maghrebine', in **Lavignac and de la Laurencie** (1921–31).

Rouanet, J. 'Les visages de la musique musulmane', *Revue musicale*, v/1 (1923).

Rouanet, J. 'La suite dans la musique musulmane', *Revue musicale*, viii/8 (1927), 280–92.

Rouanet, J. and Yafil, E. N. *Répertoire de musique arabe et maure* (1904).

Roychoudhury, M. L. 'Music in Islam', *Journal of the Royal Asiatic Society*, xxiii (1957), 101.

Sachau, E. 'Arabische Volkslieder aus Mesopotamien', *Abhandlungen der Kaiserliche Akademie der Wissenschaft Philosophisch-historisch Klasse* (1899).

Sachau, E. 'Kongress der arabischen Musik zu Kairo 1932', *Zeitschrift für Musikwissenschaft*, xiv (1931–2), 448–9.

Sachau, E. 'Das Geheimnis der babylonischen Notenschrift', *Stimmen*, i (1947–8), 236.

Sachs, C. *Real-Lexikon der Musikinstrumente* (Berlin, 1913/R1964).

Sachs, C. *Die Musikinstrumente Indiens und Indonesiens* (Berlin, 1915, 2/1923).

Sachs, C. 'Die Maultrommel', *Zeitschrift für Ethnologie*, xlix (1917), 185–200.

Sachs, C. 'Altaegyptische Musikinstrumente', *Der alte Orient*, xxi (1920).

Sachs, C. *Handbuch der Musikinstrumentenkunde* (Leipzig, 1920, 2/1930).

Sachs, C. *Die Musikinstrumente* (Breslau, 1923).

Sachs, C. *Musik des Altertums* (Breslau, 1924).

Sachs, C. *Die Musik der Antike* (Wildpark Potsdam, 1928).

Sachs, C. 'Die Marokkaner', *Zeitschrift für vergleichende Musikwissenschaft*, i (1933), 17.

Sachs, C. *The History of Musical Instruments* (New York, 1940).

Sachs, C. *The Rise of Music in the Ancient World : East and West* (New York, 1943).

Sachs, C. *The Wellsprings of Music* (The Hague, 1962).

Sachsse 'Palästinische Musikinstrumente', *Zeitschrift der deutschen Palästinavereins*, i (1927), 117.

Sadeghi, M. *Improvisation in Nonrhythmic Solo Instrumental Contemporary Persian Art Music* (MA diss., California State College, Los Angeles, 1971).

Sadokov, R. 'Muzykal'nye instrumenty drevnego Khorezma v pamiatnikakh izobrazitel'nogo iskusstva' (Ancient musical instruments of Persia in the figurative art on monuments), *Muzyka narodov Azii i Afrika* (Folk music of Asia and Africa), ed. V. S. Vinogradov (Moscow, 1969), 20–34.

Sambamoorthy, P. and others *Catalogue of Musical Instruments in the Government Museum* (Madras, 1931).

Sambamoorthy, P. and others 'AIR's seminar on the harmonium', *Sangeet natak*, xx (1971), 5–29.

Saminsky, L. 'The Music of the Peoples of the Russian Orient', *Musical Quarterly*, viii (1922), 346–52.

Sarisözen, M. 'Kaval, tulum, çifte', *Güzel San'altlar* (Ankara, 1942), 106–110.

Sastry, M. R. 'Contribution of Dakhan Muslim Princes to Indian Arts . . . Progress of Music from 779 A.D. to 1700 A.D.', *Journal of the Andhra Historical Research Society*, xxviii (1962–3), 6–8.

Sastry, M. R. 'Muslim Patrons of Music (Deccan)', *Journal of the Andhra Historical Research Society*, xxviii (1962–3), 1–6.

Saygun, A. A. 'Le recueil et la notation de la musique folklorique', *Journal of the International Folk Music Council*, i (1949), 27–32.

Schaeffner, A. *Origines des instruments de musique* (Paris, 1936).

Schaeffner, A. 'Le Tambour-sur-cadre quadrangulaire chez les noirs, d'Afrique et d'Amérique', *Colloques de Wégimont IV 1958–60 : Ethnomusicology III* (Paris, 1964), 229–48.

Scherber, F. 'Arabische Lieder', *Die Musik*, iv (1904–5).

Schlesinger, K. *Is European Musical Theory Indebted to the Arabs* (London, 1925).

Schneider, M. 'Lieder aegyptischer Bauern', *Emlékkönyv Kodály Zoltán hatvanadik születésnapjára* (Budapest, 1943), 154–8.

Schneider, M. 'A propósito de l influjo árabe : ensayo de etnografia musical de la España medieval', *Anuario musical*, i (1946), 31–143.

Schneider, M. 'Arabischer Einfluss in Spanien?', *Gesellschaft für Musikforschung Kongressbericht, Bamburg 1953* (Kassel, 1954), 175–80.

Schneider, M. 'Le verset 94 de la sourate VI du Coran étudié en une version populaire et entrios maqamât de tradition hispano-musulmane', *Anuario musical*, ix (1954), 80–96.

Schneider, M. 'Bemerkungen über die spanische Sackpfeife', *Festgabe für Hans Mersmann* (Kassel, 1957), 129–30.

Semenov, A. A. *Sredne aziatskii trakat po muzyke* (Central asiatic treatise on the music of Dervish Ali – from the 17th century) (Tashkent, 1946).

Sha'bāni, 'Azīz *Folk instruments of Iran* (in Persian) (Dept. of Culture and Arts, Shiraz University, Shiraz, 1974).

Shawki, Y. *Al-Kindi's Essay on Composition* (Cairo, 1968).

Shawki, Y. *Measuring the Arabic Music Scale* (Cairo, 1969).

Shiloah, A. *Caractéristiques de l'art vocal arabe au Moyen-Age* (Tel-Aviv, 1963).

Shiloah, A. 'Deux textes arabes inédits sur la musique' *Yuval*, i, ed. I. Adler (Jerusalem, 1968), 221–48.

Shiloah, A. 'L'Islam et la musique', in **Porte**, i (1968) 414–21.

Siedersbeck, F. 'Theater und Musik in Marokko', *Institut für Auslandsbeziehungen Zeitschrift für Kulturaustausch*, xxi (1971), 139–40.

Signell, K. 'Boomings, Jinglings, and Clangings: Turkish Influences in Western Music', *Music Educators Journal*, liv/9 (1968), 38–40.

Signell, K. *The Turkish 'Makam' System in Contemporary Theory and Practice* (diss., U. of Washington, 1973).

Signell, K. 'Esthetics of Improvisation in Turkish Art Music', *Asian Music*, v/2 (1974), 45.

Simon, A. *Studien zur aegyptischen Volksmusik* (Hamburg, 1972).

Sinha, P. 'Folk Classical Continuum in Indian Music', *Folklore*, x (1969), 355–73, 439–63 ; xi (1970), 9–19.

Sirovátka, O. 'Rozšířeni balad s tureckou tematikou v české a slovenské tradici', (The distribution of ballads with Turkish themes in Czech and Slovak tradition), *Český lid*, lv/2–3 (1968), 102–8 (German summary).

Slobin, M. S. *Instrumental Music in Northern Afghanistan* (diss., U. of Michigan, 1969).

Slobin, M. S. 'Rhythmic Aspects of the Tajīk *Maqam*', *Ethnomusicology*, xv (1971), 100–4.

Sokoli, R. *Chansons populaires albanaises* (Tirana, 1966).

Solis, T. *The Sarod: its Gat-torā Tradition with Examples by Amir Khan and Three of his Students* (MA diss., U. of Hawaii, 1970).

Sorrell, N. 'The Encyclopedia of Music and Dance in India: a Report on the Project from Bombay', *Asian Music*, iii/2 (1972), 52–4.

Southgate, T. L. 'Ancient Flutes from Egypt', *Journal of Hellenic Studies*, xxxv (1915).

Spanke, H. 'La teoria árabe sobre el origen de la lírica románica a la luz de las últimas investigaciones', *Anuario musical*, i (1946), 5–18.

Spector, J. 'Classical '*Ud* Music in Egypt with Special Reference to *Maqamat*', *Ethnomusicology*, xiv (1970), 243–57.

Stewart, R. M. *The Tablā in Perspective* (diss., U. of California, Los Angeles, 1974).

Stockmann, D., Fiedler, W. and Stockmann, E. *Albanische Volksmusik* (Berlin, 1965).

Stockmann, E. 'Die europaisichen Volksmusikinstrumente: Möglichkeiten und Probleme ihrer Darstellung in einem Handbuch', *Deutsches Jahrbuch für Volkskunde*, x (1964), 238–53.

Stockmann, E. and Uhlrich, H. 'Volksmusikinstrumente und instrumentale Volksmusik in deutschsprachigen Veröffentlichungen 1956–65', *Deutsches Jahrbuch für Volkskunde*, xii (1966), 85–101.

Stumpf, C. 'Mongolische Gesänge', *Vierteljahrschrift für Musikwissenschaft*, iii (1887); *Sammelbände für vergleichende Musikwissenschaft*, i (1922).

Sykes, P. M. 'Musical Instruments in the Khorasan', *Man*, ix (1909), 161–4.

Takacs, J. von 'Arabische Musik in Aegypten', *Der Auftakt*, ix (1929), 241.

Takeda, C. 'Songs of the Mongols, Notations and Explanations', *Journal of the Society for Research in Asiatic Music*, x–xi (December 1952), 67.

Tantawi Gawhari *Al-musiqa al-Arabiyya* (Alexandria, 1914).

Taylor, C. A. *The Physics of Musical Sound* (London, 1965).

Tewari, L. 'Turkish Village Music', *Asian Music*, iii/1 (1972), 10–24.

Thibaut, J.-B. 'Le concert classique oriental', *Bulletin française de la Société internationale de musique*, vii/1 (1911), 24–43.

Thieme, D. L. *African Music: a Briefly Annotated Bibliography* (Washington, D.C. 1964).

Thornton, P. *The Voice of Atlas: in Search of Music in Morocco* (London, 1936).

Touma, H. H. *Der Maqam Bayati im arabischen Takism* (diss., Freie Universität, Berlin, 1968).

Touma, H. H. 'The Maqam Phenomenon: an Improvisation Technique in the Music of the Middle East', *Ethnomusicology*, xv (1971), 38–48.

Touma, H. H. 'Die Türkei im 19. Jahrhundert', *Musikkulturen Asiens, Afrikas und Ozeaniens im 19. Jahrhunderts*, ed. R. Günther (Regensburg, 1973), 21–48.

Touma, H. H. *Die Musik der Arabe* (1975).

Touze, M. 'Sur les modes musulmans', *Revue musicale*, vii/1 (1925).

Trichet, P. *Traité des instruments de musique (vers 1640)* ed. F. Lesure (Neuilly-sur-Seine, 1957).

Tschakert, I. *Wandlungen persischer Tanzmusikgattungen unter westlichem Einfluss* (Hamburg, 1972).

Tsauge, G. 'A Note on the Iraqi Maqam', *Asian Music*, iv/1 (1972), 59–66.

Tsuge, G. *Āvāz: A Study of the Rhythmic Aspects in Classical Iranian Music* (diss., Wesleyan U., 1974).

Ursprung, O. 'Um die Frage nach dem arabischen bzw. maurischen Einfluss auf die abendländische Musik des Mittelalters', *Zeitschrift für Musikwissenschaft*, xvi (1934), 129–41, 355–7.

Usbeck, H. 'Türklerde musiki âletleri' (Musical instruments among the Turks), *Musiki mecmuasi*, nos. 235 (22–6); 236 (26–8); 237 (25–8); 238 (26–8); 239 (26–9); 240 (27–9); 241 (28–30); 242 (27–8); 243 (28–9) June–Feb. 1968–9.

Uysal, A. E. 'Street Cries in Turkey', *Journal of American Folklore*, no. 321 (1968), 193–215.

Varley, D. H. *African Native Music: an Annotated Bibliography* (London, 1936).

Vaziri, A. N. *Dastur-e Tar* (Berlin, 1913, 2/1936).

Vaziri, A. N. *Dastur-e Violin* (Teheran, 1933).

Vaziri, A. N. *Musiqi-ye Nazari*, ii (Teheran, 1934).

Vaziri, A. N. *Dastur-e Jadid-e Tār* (Teheran, 1936).

Verdeil, R. P. *La musique byzantine chez les Bulgares et les Russes du IXe au XIVe siècle*, Monumenta musicae byzantinae iii (1953).

Vertkov, K., ed. *Atlas muzykal'nyx instrumentov narodov SSSR* (Atlas of musical instruments of the USSR) (Moscow, 1963).

Vertkov, K. 'Muzykal'nye instrumenty kak pamiatniki istoriko-kul'turnykh sbiazei narodov' (Musical instruments as testimony of the historic-cultural relations of peoples), *Rad XV-og kongresa savenza udruženja folklorista jugoslovijc u Jajau 12–16 Septembra 1968* (Sarajevo, 1971), 321–6.

Vertkov, K., ed. *Katalog muzikal'nilch instrumentov* (Catalogue of musical instruments) (Leningrad, 1972).

Vertkov, K. 'Tipy russkikh guslei' (Types of Russian gusles), *Slavianskiĭ muzykal'nyi fol'klor* (Slavic folk music), ed. I. I. Zemtsovskii (Moscow, 1972), 275–86.

Villoteau, G. A. 'Description historique, technique et litteraire, des instruments de musique des Orientaux', *Description de l'Egypte : etat moderne* (Paris, 1809–17, 2/1826).

Villoteau, G. A. *Sur la musique en Egypte* (Paris, 1822–3).

Vinogradov, V. *Uzier Gadzhibekov i azerbajdzhanskaya muzyka* (Moscow, 1938).

Vinogradov, V. *Muzuka sovetskoj Kirgizii* (Moscow, 1939).

Vinogradov, V. 'Die musikalische Entwicklung im sowjetischen Osten', *Beiträge zur Musikwissenschaft*, ix (1967), 235–48.

Vinogradov, V. 'Zur Ethnogenese der Kirgisen im Zusammenhang mit einigen Wesenszügen ihrer Volksmusik', *Sowjetisches Volkslied- und Volksmusikforschung : ausgewählte Studien* (1967), 329–46.

Virollaud, C. and Pelagaud, F. 'La musique assyro-babylonienne', in **Lavignac and de la Laurencie** (1921–31).

Volkan, S. 'Rebáb', *Musiki mecmuasi*, no. 254 (1970), 11–13.

Vukmanović, S. 'Gusle na crnogorskom dvory' (The gusle at the court of Montenegro), *Narodno stvaralaštvo: folklor*, vii/25 (1968), 76–9.

Vyzgo, T. *Muzykal'naja kul'tura sojuznych respublik* (Musical culture in the Uzbek republic) (Moscow, 1954).

Vyzgo, T. 'O rekonstruktsii uzbekskikh narodnykh instrumentov' (About the rebuilding of Uzbeck national instruments), *Sovetskaya muzyka*, no. 12 (1954), 56.

al-Wardi, H. *Maqām al-mukhālif* (al-Mukhalef singing maqam) (Baghdad, 1969).

Wellesz, E. 'Die Kirchenmusik der Kopten und Abessinier', *Musica divina*, v (1917), 244.

Wellesz, E. *Byzantinische Musik* (Breslau, 1927).

Wellesz, E. *Eastern Elements in Western Chant* (London, 1947).

Wellesz, E. *A History of Byzantine Music and Hymnography* (Oxford, 1949, rev. 2/1961). (See bibliography for additional works on Byzantine music.)

Wellesz, E., ed. *New Oxford History of Music*, i *Ancient and Oriental Music* (London, 1957).

Werner, E. and Sonne, I. 'The Philosophy and Theory of Music in Judaeo-Arabic Literature', *Hebrew Union College Annual*, xvi (1941), 252–319; xvii (1942–3), 511–73.

Whyte, E. T. 'Egyptian Musical Instruments', *Proceedings of the Society of Biblical Archaeology*, xxi (1899).

Wilkens, E. *Künstler und Amateure im persichen Santurspiel: Studien zum Gestaltungsvermögen in der iranischen Musik* (Regensburg, 1967).

Wright, O. 'Music', *The Legacy of Islam*, ed. Bosworth and Schacht (rev. 4/1974).

Bibliography

Wright, O. 'Ibn al-Munajjim and the Early Arabian Modes', *Galpin Society Journal*, xix (1966), 27–48.

Wright, O. *'The Model System of Arabian and Persian Music, 1250–1300. An Interpretation of Contemporary Texts'* (diss., U. of London, School of Oriental and Asian Studies, 1969).

Yafil, E. and Rouanet, J. *Répertoire de musique arabe et maure : collection de mélodies* (Algiers, 1904–).

Yalgin, R. *Cenupta Türkmen Calgîlari* (Andana, 1940).

Yetka, R. 'La musique turque', in **Lavignac and de la Laurencie** (1921–31).

Yupho, D. and Moreton, D. *Thai Musical Instruments* (Bangkok, 1957).

Zataevich, A. V. *Kirgizskie instrumental'nye p'esi i napevy* (Khirgiz instrumental pieces and tunes) (Moscow, 1971).

Zatayevitsh, A. B. *250 Kirgizskikh instrumentalnykh pyes i napevov* (250 Kirghiz songs and melodies) (Moscow, 1934).

Zatayevitsh, A. B. *1000 pesen Kirgizskovo naroda* (1000 songs of the Kirghiz people (Örenburg, 1925).

Ziric, M., ed. *Junacke narodne pjesme muslimanske* (Moslem heroic folksongs) (Zagreb, 1969).

Zonis, E. *Persian Music : A Study of the History, Theory and Practice of Contemporary Art Music in Persia* (diss., Brandeis, Univ., 1968).

Zonis, E. 'Classical Persian Music in the 1960's', *Iran Faces the Seventies*, E. Yar-Shater, ed. (New York, 1971).

Zonis, E. *Classical Persian Music, an Introduction* (Cambridge, Mass., 1973).

Zoudhi, B. *L'art Syrien* (Damascus, 1972) (Hellenistic musical instruments in Syria, in Arabic).